'70

P. CLEME

Temperature Response Charts

Temperature Response Charts

by Dr. P. J. Schneider

Director of Engineering

Thermatest Laboratories, Inc.

Sunnyvale, California

John Wiley and Sons, Inc.

New York and London

Library of Congress Catalog Card Number: 63:11449
Printed in the United States of America

Preface

Present-day hardware development programs, especially those in the power-generating field and in the aircraft, missile, and spacecraft industries, are confronted with new materials application problems in the design of structures exposed to elevated heat-flux environments. These problems ultimately lead to design calculations on the temperature response of the material system to its predicted thermal environment. Although final design studies of temperature response are generally performed on automatic computers in order to take account of difficult geometry as well as variable boundary conditions and nonuniform thermal properties, there is a real need for idealized calculations in the early design stages based on exact temperature-response solutions for simple shapes. These classical constant-property solutions are especially useful for parametric studies in which the thermal properties and thicknesses of material, and the heat input and heating duration are systematically varied to determine temperature response sensitivity, peak surface and back-face temperatures, and the like. Thus, because many relatively complicated components can be realistically approximated by the simple body shapes, the classical heat-conduction solutions assume a role of genuine technical importance in preliminary hardware design studies.

The exact solutions are, however, frequently neglected in parametric design studies because of the laborious hand calculations involved in repetitive evaluations of the series solutions. For this reason recourse is often made to graphed results based on parametric evaluations of the exact solutions. But a dependence on graphed results is often hampered by one of several reasons. First, only a few of the total number of useful exact solutions are available in the graphed form of temperature-time curves, and these are widely dispersed in the engineering literature. Second, the graphs are not plotted in a consistent fashion, nor are the basic independent and dependent variables and parameters expressed in a uniform nomenclature. Last, the numerical data are not always graphed over the total range of variables and parameters of interest with the result that curves must be extrapolated and/or answers obtained in a portion of the curve family in which graphical accuracy is difficult if not impossible to achieve.

The present collection of charts was prepared in an effort to overcome these difficulties and to bring together under a single format the widespread numerical results on transient heat conduction in thermal systems of fundamental practical interest. In the course of this undertaking it has been possible to systematize this information as to problem class and the range of variables and parameters covered. Of equal importance to users of these data is the fact that a single collection results in a general consistency of nomenclature and method of graphical presentation that is lacking in individual collections of heat-conduction papers from the open literature.

As to the organization of material, it is clear that only a fraction of the total number of available solutions could be selected for presentation. In making this selection, only those solutions based on one-dimensional heat flow with constant material properties were chosen. This reduced the graphical problem to display of a set of independent and dependent variables and one or two parameters (in one case four). Of the solutions remaining, the ones chosen were those which in my experience were most frequently needed in practice. In many cases this naturally coincided with the solutions for which numerical results were already available, while in other cases the numerical results had to be calculated. In the few cases where exact solutions were not available, the temperature response was calculated by means of an approximate integral solution.

A total of 120 charts are given, covering temperature response of the simple shapes under a variety of boundary conditions and for a wide range of the characteristic Fourier and Biot numbers. The body shapes considered include the semi-infinite solid, the single- and two-layer plate, the solid and hollow cylinder and sphere, the cylindrical and spherical cavity, and the ellipse and ellipsoids. Boundary conditions include constant and variable surface temperature, constant and variable ambient temperature, constant and variable heat input, and radiation. All data are plotted in a uniform format and set of symbols. The choice of coordinates, namely, rectilinear for temperature and logarithmic for time, produces a family of curves that is as easily read at small as at large exposure times. This is in contrast to the conventional log-temperature, rectilinear-time representation in which reading accuracy is sacrificed in the early period of heating for the plotting convenience of straight lines in the later period.

Production of the charts was accomplished by careful pencil plotting of the temperature-time data on fine-grid commercial graphpaper, inking the curves directly, and then photographing the result. This method (used in place of tracing) serves the dual purpose of preserving accuracy of the plotted data and providing a fine, accurate background subdivision that could not be obtained by inking a traced grid. This close background greatly assists in taking data from the curves and in interpolating between parameters.

I hope that the collection will be of use to students and practicing thermal engineers as well as to others in industry who have need for temperature-response estimates but who do not necessarily have the direct computational experience. If users of the charts are aware of other data which should be included, or if this book stimulates the evaluation of additional solutions that are of practical interest but lacking at this time, I would appreciate being informed of these results in order to include them in subsequent editions.

P. J. SCHNEIDER

Los Altos, California
February 1963

Contents

1

Introduction

The charts presented in this book represent analytical solutions for transient, one-dimensional heat conduction in bodies of fundamental geometric shape. Only those solutions are graphed for which the properties of density, specific heat, and thermal conductivity for the conducting material are isotropic and constant (i.e., the same in every direction and independent of the material's instantaneous temperature). While most of these solutions are mathematically exact, a few of the charts are based on approximate numerical and integral methods of solution.

Although the chief purpose of the charts is concerned with the problem of predicting surface and internal temperature transients in hardware components, they are also useful for thermal stress analyses, in the design of research apparatus, and for data interpretation in studies of surface heat transfer by convection and/or radiation. Another use arises in materials studies in which thermal properties are deduced from laboratory temperature-response measurements in the simple body shapes.

2

Nomenclature

The complete set of symbols used in the charts are defined in the text illustrations and in the following list of nomenclature. Groups of symbols are also defined in the charts themselves because such dimensionless groups as T, Fo, Bi, X, and R, although consistent in form, vary in specific detail from chart to chart depending on geometry, boundary conditions, and the like. The units shown are illustrative only; any consistent set of units may be adopted.

English:

a = semimajor diameter of ellipse, ft

Bi = Biot number = $h\delta/k$, hr_i/k, hr_e/k, hb/k

b = semiminor diameter of ellipse, ft

C = specific heat of body material, Btu/lb-°F

C_t = specific heat of fluid coolant, transpiration cooling, Btu/lb-°F

c = constant

∂ = partial derivative

E = exact solution

e = constant = 2.71828

Fo = Fourier number = $\alpha\theta/\delta^2$, $\alpha\theta/r_i^2$, $\alpha\theta/r_e^2$, $\alpha\theta/b^2$

Fo′ = modified Fourier number (based on period of heating) = $\alpha P/\delta^2$, $\alpha P/2\pi\delta^2$

F_A = radiation surface configuration factor

F_ϵ = radiation surface emissivity factor

G_t = mass flow rate of fluid coolant, transpiration cooling, lb/hr-ft²

g = coolant flow parameter, transpiration cooling = $G_t C_t \delta/k$

h = convective unit surface conductance, Btu/hr-ft²-°F

I = integral solution

i = integers = 0, 1, 2, . . .

j = even integers = 0, 2, 4, . . .

k = thermal conductivity of body material, Btu/hr-ft-°F

L = body length, ft

M = radiation parameter = $\sigma F_A F_\epsilon t_0^3 \delta / k$

m = internal conductance ratio of two-layer plate = $(k_2/\delta_2)/(k_1/\delta_1)$

N = numerical solution

n = internal heat capacity ratio of two-layer plate = $\rho_2 C_2 \delta_2 / \rho_1 C_1 \delta_1$

P = period (duration) of heating, period of harmonic temperature wave, hr

p = odd integers = 1, 3, 5, . . .

Q = total heat input = $\int_0^P q\, d\theta$, Btu/ft²

q = rate of heat input, Btu/hr-ft²

R = radius ratio = r/r_i, r/r_e

r = radius, ft

s = constant

T = dimensionless temperature

$\overline{T}$ = dimensionless mean temperature

t = temperature, °F, °R in radiation solutions

$\bar{t}$ = mean temperature, °F

X = depth ratio = x/δ

x = depth, ft

Z_p = temperature response function

∞ = infinitely large

$+$ = or greater

$-$ = or less

Greek:

α = thermal diffusivity of body material = $k/\rho C$, ft²/hr

δ = plate thickness, ft

ϵ = eccentricity of ellipse = $\sqrt{1 - (b/a)^2}$, radiation surface emissivity

θ = time, hr

μ = two-layer plate parameter = $n + (n + 1)/\text{Bi}_1$

π = constant = 3.14159

ρ = density of body material, lb/ft³

σ = Stefan-Boltzmann radiation constant = 17.3×10^{-10}, Btu/hr-ft²-°R⁴

Subscripts:

A – configuration

a – ambient fluid

c – center

e – external surface

i – internal surface

max – maximum

r — thermal response
s — radiation source or sink
t — transpiration fluid
0 — initial ($\theta < 0$)
1 — first (front) layer of two-layer plate
2 — second (back) layer of two-layer plate
$*$ — amplitude of surface temperature wave
ϵ — emissivity

3

Layout of Charts

The charts are arranged according to boundary condition, the relative magnitude of internal-to-surface conductance, and body shape. Individual cases considered in each of these three categories are:

A. *Boundary Condition*
    (1) Constant surface temperature.
    (2) Variable surface temperature.
    (3) Constant ambient temperature.
    (4) Constant and variable heat input.
    (5) Radiation.

B. *Body Shape*
    (*a*) Semi-infinite solid.
    (*b*) Single-layer plate.
    (*c*) Two-layer plate.
    (*d*) Cylinder.
    (*e*) Cylindrical cavity.
    (*f*) Cylindrical shell.
    (*g*) Sphere.
    (*h*) Spherical cavity.
    (*i*) Spherical shell.
    (*j*) Ellipse.
    (*k*) Ellipsoids.

C. *Internal and Surface Conductance*
    (i) Finite internal conductance, infinite surface conductance.
    (ii) Infinite internal conductance, finite surface conductance.
    (iii) Finite internal and surface conductance.
    (iv) Finite internal conductance.
    (v) Infinite internal conductance.

All combinations of A and C are not possible. The cases 1-v and 2-v, for example, are trivial. In addition, not all the boundary conditions in A

are treated with each of the geometries in B. But for all cases considered each chart is presented in the order A-B-C listed above. The following tabulation in Table 1 gives the order of cases treated and the charts included by figure number:

Table 1. *Order of Chart Placement*

Cases	Charts
1-B-i	1–13
2-B-i	14–18
3-B-ii	19–21
3-B-iii	22–40
4-B-iv	41–49
4-B-v	50
5-B-iv	51–52
5-B-v	53

A majority of the charts are seen to be for the convection boundary condition with constant ambient temperature and finite internal and surface conductance. Only a limited number of variable surface-temperature solutions are given in comparison to the constant surface-temperature solutions. The reason for this is that once the constant surface-temperature solutions are known, similar results for prescribed variable surface temperature can be obtained by superposition or use of Duhamel's theorem.

4

Description of Charts

As necessary background for interpretation of the temperature-time data, typical governing heat conduction equations are reviewed, and a detailed description is given of the body shapes, boundary conditions, parameters, and method of plotting used in preparing the charts.

Governing Equations

Assume ρ, C, and k as constants for the conducting material, and consider only materials free of heat sources or sinks. Consider, in addition, only those geometries and boundary conditions for which the heat flow in the conducting body is one-dimensional. Then the partial-differential equations for the temperature history in, for example, a plate, $t(x,\theta)$, and a cylinder, $t(r,\theta)$, are respectively

$$\frac{\partial^2}{\partial x^2} t(x,\theta) = \frac{1}{\alpha} \frac{\partial}{\partial \theta} t(x,\theta) \tag{1}$$

and

$$\frac{\partial^2}{\partial r^2} t(r,\theta) + \frac{1}{r} \frac{\partial}{\partial r} t(r,\theta) = \frac{1}{\alpha} \frac{\partial}{\partial \theta} t(r,\theta), \tag{2}$$

where $\alpha = k/\rho C$ is the constant thermal diffusivity of the conducting material.

Characteristic dimensionless variables may be introduced by normalizing Equations 1 and 2 for the plate and cylinder as

$$\frac{\partial^2}{\partial X^2} T(X,\mathrm{Fo}) = \frac{\partial}{\partial \mathrm{Fo}} T(X,\mathrm{Fo})$$

and $\qquad \dfrac{\partial^2}{\partial R^2} T(R,\text{Fo}) + \dfrac{1}{R} \dfrac{\partial}{\partial R} T(R,\text{Fo}) = \dfrac{\partial}{\partial \text{Fo}} T(R,\text{Fo}).$

Here $T = (t - t_0)/(t_a - t_0)$, or some other form of dimensionless temperature, depending on boundary condition, is the dependent variable. For a plate $\text{Fo} = \alpha\theta/\delta^2$, the Fourier number, is the dimensionless time variable, and $X = x/\delta$ is the dimensionless depth coordinate. Similarily, for a cylinder $\text{Fo} = \alpha\theta/r_e^2$ and $R = r/r_e$. In both cases Fo and X (or Fo and R) are independent variables. Generally Fo is retained as the single independent variable with X (or R) treated as a parameter.

Solutions of the above equations, and others in spherical and elliptical coordinates, give the temperature response (temperature-time relation) of the various body shapes with various impressed boundary conditions. The charts graphically display these solutions for a wide range of the independent time variable and characteristic parameters that are dependent on body shape, relative internal conductance, and boundary condition.

Body Shapes

The eleven body shapes listed in Article 3 (p.5) are sketched in Fig. 1. The semi-infinite solid (a) is infinite in the vertical, normal, and x directions. The single- and two-layer plates (b) and (c) are infinite in the vertical and normal directions. The cylinder (d) may be a solid disk with thermally insulated ends or a solid cylindrical rod of infinite length. The sphere (g) is solid. The cylindrical cavity (e) is infinite in the r direction and likewise may be an insulated infinite disk with a central hole or an infinitely long cylindrical hole in a large body. The spherical cavity (h) is infinite in the r direction and represents a spherical hole in a large body. The cylindrical shell (f) may be a ring (washer) with insulated faces or an infinitely long tube. The spherical shell (i) is a hollow sphere. The ellipse (j) may be an elliptical disk with insulated faces or a solid elliptical rod of infinite length. The solid ellipsoids (k) are ellipses of revolution, a prolate spheroid if rotated about a and an oblate spheroid if rotated about b. It is understood that the term infinite extent infers largeness relative to other characteristic body dimensions. It is this characteristic along with uniform surface heating that allows the assumption of one-dimensional heat conduction in these geometrically symmetrical bodies.

The essential difference between the rectangular and cylindrical (or spherical) coordinate systems shown is in the choice of origin. For the semi-infinite solid and the plate $x = 0$ is at the exposed heat-input surface, while in the cylindrical and spherical geometries the origin $r = 0$ is always at the center of symmetry. The two-layer plate has two coordinates x_1 and x_2 adopted for convenience in describing depth locations in either solid. In the charts the single-layer plate is referred to simply as a plate, while the two-layer plate is identified as such.

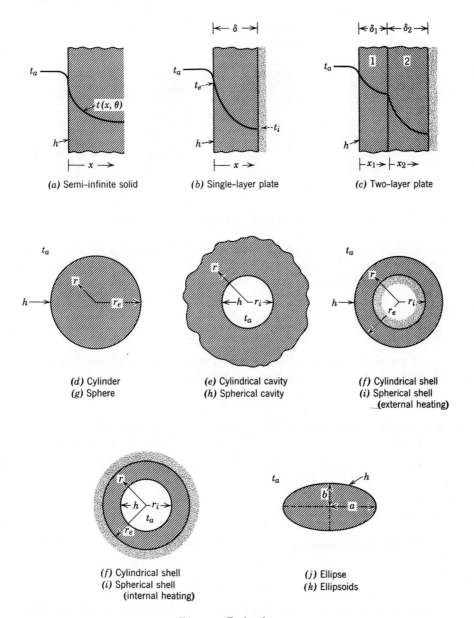

(a) Semi-infinite solid (b) Single-layer plate (c) Two-layer plate

(d) Cylinder
(g) Sphere

(e) Cylindrical cavity
(h) Spherical cavity

(f) Cylindrical shell
(i) Spherical shell
  (external heating)

(f) Cylindrical shell
(i) Spherical shell
  (internal heating)

(j) Ellipse
(k) Ellipsoids

Fig. 1. Body shapes.

Boundary Conditions

The classes of boundary conditions considered in the charts include convection, prescribed heat input, and radiation. All illustrations in Fig. 1 are for the convection boundary condition only.

The separate input data needed to describe all three boundary conditions are shown in Fig. 2 for a single-layer plate. The point shading here and in Fig. 1 at the back surface $x = \delta$ indicates an adiabatic (ther-

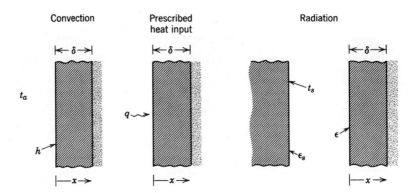

Fig. 2.   Surface heating boundary conditions.

mally insulated) surface as a second boundary condition.   A third boundary condition, called the initial condition, is the temperature state of the body prior to heating or cooling.

Initial condition

All the charts are based on an initial condition of uniform temperature throughout the conducting body.   Thus, for a plate

$$t(x, \theta < 0) = t_0, \tag{3}$$

where t_0 is a constant initial temperature.   Likewise for a cylindrical shell (tube)

$$t(r, \theta < 0) = t_0. \tag{4}$$

Adiabatic boundary condition

The adiabatic condition for the back face of a plate is

$$\frac{\partial}{\partial x} t(\delta, \theta) = 0. \tag{5}$$

For the cylindrical shell two conditions exist depending on whether heating occurs externally or internally (Fig. 1).   For the former

$$\frac{\partial}{\partial r} t(r_i, \theta) = 0 \tag{6}$$

and for the latter

$$\frac{\partial}{\partial r} t(r_e, \theta) = 0. \tag{7}$$

Natural adiabatic conditions arise in certain geometries with uniform heating.   For the semi-infinite solid $x \geq 0$ an adiabatic plane exists at some minimum depth x for $\theta < \infty$ where the surface heat input is not yet felt. If a plate $0 \leq x \leq 2\delta$ is heated uniformly and equally at each exposed face, then $x = \delta$ is adiabatic. The center of a cylinder or sphere which is heated uniformly is an adiabatic line or point.

Convection boundary condition

Considering a flat plate as in (b) of Fig. 1, the condition of heat input by convection at $x = 0$ from a fluid stream of temperature t_a (Fig. 2) is

$$h[t_a - t(0,\theta)] = -k\left[\frac{\partial}{\partial x} t(0,\theta)\right]. \tag{8}$$

In the charts for this boundary condition the ambient temperature t_a is assumed to be uniform away from the exposed plate surface, and the unit surface conductance h is assumed constant over the surface $x = 0$. The negative sign in Equation 8 arises because heating is considered, and as a consequence t diminishes with increasing x as illustrated in (a), (b), and (c) of Fig. 1. For cooling $\partial t/\partial x$ is positive, but $t_a - t$ is negative. For heating of a cylinder as in (d) of Fig. 1

$$h[t_a - t(r_e,\theta)] = k\left[\frac{\partial}{\partial r} t(r_e,\theta)\right]. \tag{9}$$

Here $\partial t/\partial r$ is positive for heating owing to the reversed coordinate r compared to x.

The interpretation of t_a depends on the flow velocity of the convective stream. For low-speed flow, t_a is the local temperature of the thermally undisturbed free-stream flow. For high-speed flow, t_a is the adiabatic-wall (recovery) temperature which depends on the recovery factor, local temperature, specific heats, and Mach number of the flow.

The convection boundary condition introduces a second parameter, the Biot number $\mathrm{Bi} = h\delta/k$. This is apparent after normalizing Equation 8 using $T = (t - t_0)/(t_a - t_0)$ as

$$\mathrm{Bi}[1 - T(0,\mathrm{Fo})] = -\frac{\partial}{\partial X} T(0,\mathrm{Fo}). \tag{10}$$

Considering a plate of unit surface area, the Biot number may be rewritten as $\mathrm{Bi} = h/(k/\delta)$ and thus interpreted as the ratio of surface-to-internal thermal conductance. Heat conduction solutions are greatly simplified if temperature gradients through the conducting material can be neglected (i.e., if $\partial T/\partial X = 0$ for all X). This implies a high internal thermal conductance. In the charts this condition is denoted as $k \to \infty$ even though $\delta \to 0$ gives the same result. The reason for choosing this designation is that the solutions neglecting internal temperature gradients are independent of k but not of δ.

The case of constant surface temperature ($t_e = \mathrm{const}$) is a special case of the convection boundary condition for which $h \to \infty$ and thereby $t_e = t_a$.

Prescribed heat input boundary condition

In many problems h and t_a are functions of θ. Under these conditions all quantities on the left side of Equation 8 are dependent on time. It then becomes more convenient to express the boundary condition (Fig. 2) as

$$q_{x=0} = q(\theta) = -k\left[\frac{\partial}{\partial x}\, t(0,\theta)\right], \qquad (11)$$

where $q(\theta)$ is some prescribed heat-input function.

The prescribed heat-input boundary condition is useful, for example, in problems of aerodynamic heating where h and t_a vary with altitude and Mach number. For low Mach numbers (e.g., missile atmospheric exit-phase flight) $t_a(\theta)$ and $t(0,\theta)$ are of the same order of magnitude so $q(\theta) = h(\theta)[t_a(\theta) - t(0,\theta)]$ must be obtained by solution for $t(0,\theta)$ over small time steps. In this case the heat input is surface-temperature dependent. For high Mach numbers (e.g., missile atmospheric re-entry flight) the temperature potential $[t_a(\theta) - t(0,\theta)]$ is primarily a function of $t_a(\theta)$ and, consequently, $q(\theta)$ can be determined before and independent of the conduction problem. The prescribed heat-input boundary condition is also useful in certain forms of controlled electrical heating where a contact resistance heater transfers all of its electrically generated heat to the surface of the body. This is another example where q or $q(\theta)$ can be uniquely determined because the heat input is effectively independent of the receiver's surface temperature.

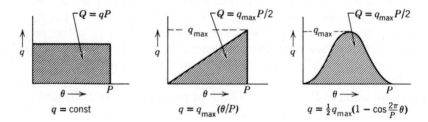

Fig. 3. Example heat-input functions.

A few typical heat-input functions $q(\theta)$ are illustrated in Fig. 3. Here P is the period (duration) of heating, the total heat input in this period being $Q = \int_0^P q\, d\theta$. By way of example, the first two $q(\theta)$ functions, the constant heat input and the linearly increasing heat input, are useful in electrical heating applications, while the third is applicable in describing missile aerodynamic heating pulses.

Radiation boundary condition

Consider again a single-layer plate as in (b) of Fig. 1. The condition of heat input at the receiver surface by radiation from a heat source at constant temperature t_s (Fig. 2) is

$$\sigma F_A F_\epsilon [t_s^4 - t^4(0,\theta)] = -k \left[\frac{\partial}{\partial x} t(0,\theta) \right]. \qquad (12)$$

Here σ is a constant and all temperatures t are absolute. The constants F_A and F_ϵ are functions of geometry (source and receiver) and the surface emissivities ϵ_s and ϵ. The factor F_A takes into account the geometry and relative position of the source and receiver surfaces, and F_ϵ accounts for nonideal radiators and absorbing media between the source and receiver.

Normalizing Equation 12 produces a characteristic radiation parameter containing the above properties. Thus, with $T = t/t_0$,

$$M[T_s^4 - T^4(0,\text{Fo})] = - \frac{\partial}{\partial X} T(0,\text{Fo}). \qquad (13)$$

The parameter $M = \sigma F_A F_\epsilon t_0^3 \delta / k$, although yet unnamed after an original investigator, is seen to be analogous to the Biot number $\text{Bi} = h\delta/k$ for the convection boundary condition. By this analogy the unit surface conductance h for radiation is $\sigma F_A F_\epsilon t_0^3$.

Parameters

The dependent variable in the charts is always the dimensionless temperature T plotted as ordinate. The exact form of T depends on the boundary condition, body shape, and the relative magnitude of internal conductance. The independent variable, plotted as abscissa, always contains the Fourier number Fo. Its form, like T, is also dependent on the above conditions, as is the form and number of parameters.

Table 2 gives a skeleton tabulation of the various independent variables and parameters that arise with different boundary conditions, body shape and relative internal conductance. Only the semi-infinite solid and plate geometries are shown, and not all the variations in a given boundary condition are tabulated.

It is apparent from Table 2 that the plate always has one more parameter than the semi-infinite solid, both bodies being of finite conductivity. For example, for constant surface temperature ($t_e = \text{const}$) the independent variable is $X/\sqrt{\text{Fo}}$ for the semi-infinite solid, and thus all depths in X and all times in Fo can be displayed without any parameters. But for the same case with a plate the former independent variable $X/\sqrt{\text{Fo}}$ is decoupled and Fo becomes the independent variable with X a parameter. The case of constant ambient temperature adds a parameter to both the semi-infinite solid and plate, $X/\sqrt{\text{Fo}}$ for the former and Bi for the latter. The case of infinite conductivity reduces the number of plate parameters to one less than the semi-infinite solid with (necessarily) $k \neq \infty$. The prescribed heat-input boundary condition follows the same pattern except that two sets of independent variables and parameters appear, depending on whether q is or is not constant. For $k \neq \infty$ and a given heat input

Table 2. Example Independent Variables and Parameters

BODY SHAPE	BOUNDARY CONDITION	CONDUCTIVITY	INDEPENDENT VARIABLE	PARAMETERS
Semi-infinite solid	$t_e = $ const	$k \neq \infty$	$X/\sqrt{\mathrm{Fo}}$	–
Plate	$t_e = $ const	$k \neq \infty$	Fo	X
Semi-infinite solid	$t_a = $ const	$k \neq \infty$	$\mathrm{Bi}\sqrt{\mathrm{Fo}}$	$X/\sqrt{\mathrm{Fo}}$
Plate	$t_a = $ const	$k \neq \infty$	Fo	X, Bi
Plate	$t_a = $ const	$k = \infty$	BiFo	–
Semi-infinite solid	$q = $ const	$k \neq \infty$	$X/\sqrt{\mathrm{Fo}}$	–
Semi-infinite solid	$q \neq $ const	$k \neq \infty$	$X/\sqrt{\mathrm{Fo}}$	Fo/Fo'
Plate	$q = $ const	$k \neq \infty$	Fo	X
Plate	$q \neq $ const	$k \neq \infty$	Fo/Fo'	X, Fo'
Plate	$q = $ const	$k = \infty$	Fo/Fo'	–
Plate	$q \neq $ const	$k = \infty$	Fo/Fo'	–
Semi-infinite solid	$t_s = $ const	$k \neq \infty$	$M^2\mathrm{Fo}$	X, T_s
Plate	$t_s = $ const	$k \neq \infty$	Fo	X, T_s, M
Plate	$t_s = $ const	$k = \infty$	$MT_s^3\mathrm{Fo}$	T_s

(constant or variable) the plate has one more parameter than the semi-infinite solid as before. But for $k \neq \infty$ and a given geometry the number of parameters is increased by one in going from a constant to a variable heat input. The exception is for $k = \infty$; here no parameters are needed for either heat input. The radiation boundary condition has the characteristics already noted, but on comparison with the analogous case of convection ($t_a = $ const) it is apparent that all geometries and relative conductivities lead to an additional parameter. This is a result of the nonlinear temperature potential in radiation problems.

The maximum number of parameters shown in Table 2 is increased by one when considering the cylindrical shell or ellipse, for in these cases the radius ratio R_i or eccentricity ϵ forms an additional parameter. The two-layer plate adds two parameters over the usual two (X and Bi) for the case of $t_a = $ const. The maximum number of parameters in the charts, namely four, is for this case of a two-layer plate with the convection boundary condition. In order to display this case with reasonable economy of space, the Fourier number was combined with two of the four parameters in a way that compresses the time scale into one cycle on the logarithmic abscissa.

In a few cases (notably the cylindrical and spherical shells) temperature-response curves for both surfaces are presented on the same chart to conserve space. Surface temperatures are given preference when too many charts would be required to generate curves for intermediate wall stations X or R.* In other cases involving more than one parameter, a sufficient

---

*Unfortunately, there is no simple relation whereby internal temperatures can be computed from surface temperatures valid for all Fourier and Biot numbers. Where internal temperatures are not given, however, approximate results can be obtained graphically from a dimensionless plot of $T(X)$ at a given Fourier number, noting that the curve must satisfy the heat input and adiabatic surface boundary conditions.

number of charts is given to permit cross-plotting for intermediate values of the second and/or additional parameters. The plate, being of greatest technical interest, is treated more thoroughly for intermediate values of X and for high and low Fourier and Biot numbers.

Method of Plotting

The charts are graphed as dimensionless temperature versus dimensionless time. The single exception to this is Chart 49 in which the heat input is of such general form that dimensionless temperature could not be plotted explicitly.

A majority of the charts are plotted with rectilinear ordinate and logarithmic abscissa for boundary conditions 1, 3 and 5 (Article 3, p. 5). The charts for boundary conditions 2 and 4 are plotted with both rectilinear ordinate and abscissa. A general convention of the past has been to plot charts for boundary conditions 1 and 3 with logarithmic ordinate and rectilinear abscissa. This method has the advantage that the curves develop into straight lines at the higher Fourier numbers. However, at the low Fourier numbers which are usually of considerable practical interest (especially with thermal insulating materials) the curves tend to bunch together and become unreadable. Also, the usual convention is to plot dimensionless temperature as $T = (t - t_a)/(t_0 - t_a)$ for the convection boundary condition and to specify the heat-transfer parameter as $1/\text{Bi}$. The present charts for this case are presented on rectilinear-logarithmic coordinates with $T = (t - t_0)/(t_a - t_0)$ and with Bi displayed directly.* This method has a number of advantages. First, although the former straight lines (which are straight lines for all Fourier numbers in the special case of $k \to \infty$) now develop into S curves, each curve is as easily read at the low as at the high Fourier numbers. Thus temperature ratios near $T = 0$ and $T = 1$ are readily distinguishable, whereas by the old method it was often impossible to read temperature ratios between $T = 0.8$ and $T = 1$. The adoption of $T = (t - t_0)/(t_a - t_0)$, although applicable to either heating or cooling, gives a family of curves which appears to apply to conditions of heating (i.e., temperature increasing with time). These are more easily interpreted than apparent cooling curves. Finally, from the physical meaning of the Biot number (Article 4, p. 11) it is easier to interpret increasing or decreasing values of $\text{Bi} = h\delta/k$ than its reciprocal $1/\text{Bi}$. For this reason the Biot number is displayed directly rather than inverted.

*The rectilinear-logarithmic coordinate system for plotting temperature-response data seems to have been first used by H. Groeber (1925), but T vs Bi with Fo as parameter was used rather than T vs Fo with Bi a parameter, as in the present charts. Groeber's method has the advantage that in practice the need for interpolation generally occurs in the Biot number. The disadvantage in plotting this way is that the data loses its usual temperature-time significance, and consistency with plots for other boundary conditions is lost.

As a consequence of the constant-property assumption, all curves hold equally in heating or cooling for boundary conditions 1, 2, 3, and 4 (Article 3, p. 5). For prescribed heat removal rather than heat addition, q is simply replaced by $-q$. With boundary condition 5, heating and cooling represent individual cases and separate curves are given for each.

The properties ρ, C and k refer to the conducting materials in all cases. For a two-layer plate these properties are identified with one or the other layer by use of subscripts. An exception to the meaning of these properties arises in the case of a porous transpiration-cooled plate. Here the symbols ρ, C and k represent effective properties which are functions of the porosity of the plate material and of the analogous properties of the fluid coolant.

All curves in the charts were plotted and inked on fine-line commercial graphpaper and photographed directly. The result is a dense but easily read background of fine coordinate grid lines for accurate readoff of plotted temperature-time data.

The total number of charts is 120, based on 53 problem solutions.* Titles for each of these charts are listed by order of presentation in Article 6. Reference to this list of charts, to the body shapes in Fig. 1 of Article 4, and to the nomenclature in Article 2 is sufficient to identify all 53 solutions as to geometry, boundary condition, relative conductivity, and the necessary constants for explicitly calculating body temperature t at any time θ. A narrow black page border assists in quickly locating these key information pages.

The charts (1 through 53) are given in Article 7.

References to published works on temperature-response solutions and/or numerical results are listed by order of use in Article 8. The reference or references used (if any) in a given chart are listed at the end of each chart title in Article 6. In some cases the reference refers to the original or a convenient source of the solution itself, while in other instances it refers to the source of either calculated or plotted data. A number of the charts are the result of combining data from several sources. In a few cases several sources for the same data are cited in Article 8 while only one is used in the chart title of Article 6. This is done to give credit to earlier investigators of the same problem, and in some instances to put the reader in touch with additional data not included here.

*Examples in use of the charts are given in Article 5.

5

Example Use of Charts

A number of sample problems are solved to illustrate application of the charts and use of the nomenclature evaluated with typical engineering dimensional units.

EXAMPLE 1. The average thermal diffusivity of a material between 70 and 400°F is to be determined by measuring the insulated back-face temperature response of a 0.25″-thick flat sample of the material heated at its front face with a variable heat input which raises its front-face temperature linearly with time. Calculate the material's average diffusivity from the measured face temperatures in Fig. 4.

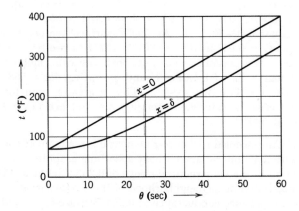

Fig. 4. Diffusivity measurement.

Solution. Since the heated-surface temperature rise is linear as $t_e = t_0 + c\theta$, Chart 16 applies. From Fig. 4, $c = 5.5$°F/sec and at $x = \delta$ for, say, $\theta = 60$ sec, $t = 322$°F. By using Chart 16, $T = (t - t_0)/c\theta = (322 - 70)/5.5 \times 60 = 0.764$ for $X = 1$, and thus Fo = 2.11 = $\alpha\theta/\delta^2$ from which $\alpha = 2.11(0.25/12)^2/(60/3600) = 0.055$ ft²/hr.

EXAMPLE 2. A simple "thin-skin" capacitance calorimeter is used to measure the unit surface conductance and heat rate in stagnation-point flow of the gas in a blowdown wind-tunnel test facility in which the adiabatic wall (recovery) temperature of the flow is 3100°F. The calorimeter is constructed of a thin copper disk $\frac{1}{16}''$ thick, one face being insulated and the other exposed to the flow. A thermocouple embedded halfway through the disk thickness monitors the calorimeter temperature response during sudden exposure to the flow (Fig. 5). On post-test examination of the temperature trace, data above 500°F were discarded to eliminate re-radiation effects at the heated face of the calorimeter. If the calorimeter temperature rose from 70°F to 500°F in one second, estimate: (*a*) the unit surface conductance (assumed constant), and (*b*) the heat rate attained in the flow at surface temperatures of 500°F.

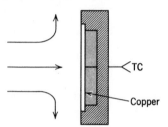

Fig. 5.   Calorimeter.

Solution. The copper disk, being flat, thin and of high thermal conductivity can be considered to respond as a plate of infinite internal thermal conductance. As such, Curve 1 of Chart 19 applies assuming h to be constant during heating. (*a*) From the data $\delta = \frac{1}{16}''$, $t_a = 3100°F$, $t_0 = 70°F$ and $t = 500°F$ at $\theta = 1$ sec. For copper $\rho = 558$ lb/ft³ and $C = 0.092$ Btu/lb-°F. Then at 1 second, $T = (t - t_0)/(t_a - t_0) = (500 - 70)/(3100 - 70) = 0.142$, and from Chart 19 BiFo $= 0.154 = h\theta/\rho C\delta$, from which $h = 0.154 \times 558 \times 0.092(1/16 \times 12)/1 = 0.0412$ Btu/sec-ft²-°F. (*b*) At 500°F surface temperature the heat rate is $q = h(t_a - t) = 0.0412(3100 - 500) = 107$ Btu/sec-ft². If the heat input from the flow were assumed constant, then the calorimeter temperature rise would be linear (Chart 50, Curve 1) and $q = \rho C\delta \, dt/d\theta = 558 \times 0.092(1/16 \times 12)(500 - 70)/1 = 115$ Btu/sec-ft². This is greater than for constant h because in that case the calorimeter temperature $t(\theta)$ heels over and the value of $dt/d\theta$ is less at 500°F.

EXAMPLE 3.   An uncooled rocket-engine nozzle is made up of concentric cylindrical tubes with a 4″ inner-diameter heat-absorbing graphite liner of $\frac{1}{2}''$ wall thickness backed up by a steel structural sleeve of 0.26″ thickness (Fig. 6). The heat input is a maximum in the neighborhood of the nozzle throat with an estimated convective unit surface conductance of 0.204 Btu/sec-ft²-°F and an exhaust gas

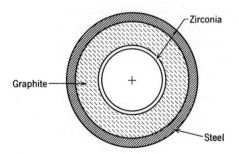

Fig. 6.   Nozzle wall.

temperature of 4500°F. If the graphite liner temperature must be limited to 3500°F to minimize erosion from the high-speed exhaust flow, compute the allowable burning time for the engine by: (*a*) neglecting heat flow into the steel sleeve, (*b*) accounting for heat flow into the steel sleeve, and (*c*) neglecting heat flow into the steel sleeve and retaining the graphite temperature limit of 3500°F, but considering that the inner surface of the graphite liner is protected by a low-conductivity, high melting-point stabilized zirconia coating of 0.071″ thickness.

Solution. (*a*) Without heat conduction into the steel sleeve, the outer surface of the graphite may be assumed adiabatic. In this case Chart 36(*d*) applies with $R_i = r_i/r_e = 2.0/2.5 = 0.8$. For graphite $\rho = 105$ lb/ft³, $C = 0.344$ Btu/lb-°F, and $k = 0.0106$ Btu/sec-ft-°F, so $\alpha = 0.000294$ ft²/sec. From the given data, $\mathrm{Bi} = hr_e/k = 0.204(2.5/12)/0.0106 = 4$ and $T_{\mathrm{allow}} = (t_{\mathrm{allow}} - t_0)/(t_a - t_0) = (3500 - 70)/(4500 - 70) = 0.775$. Using the curves $r = r_i$ in Chart 36(*d*), $\mathrm{Fo} = 0.088 = \alpha\theta/r_e^2$ and the allowable burning time becomes $\theta_{\mathrm{allow}} = 0.088 \times (2.5/12)^2/0.000294 = 13.0$ sec. (*b*) Since a solution is not given in the charts for a two-layer cylindrical shell, the two-layer plate solution of Chart 31 will be used. The error incurred may be estimated by solution of the problem in (*a*), using the single-layer plate. In this case $\delta = 0.5″$, $\mathrm{Bi} = h\delta/k = 0.204(0.5/12)/0.0106 = 0.8$ and $X = 0$. Using Chart 23(*a*) with $T = 0.775$, $\mathrm{Fo} = 2.1 = \alpha\theta/\delta^2$ and $\theta_{\mathrm{allow}} = 2.1(0.5/12)^2/0.000294 = 12.4$ sec. This is close enough to 13.0 sec to justify use of the plate solutions. For steel, $\rho = 480$ lb/ft³, $C = 0.147$ Btu/lb-°F, and $k = 0.00555$ Btu/sec-ft-°F, so $m = (k_2/\delta_2)/(k_1/\delta_1) = (0.00555/0.26)/(0.0106/0.50) = 1$. Thus, Chart 31(*a*) applies with $n = \rho_2 C_2 \delta_2/\rho_1 C_1 \delta_1 = (480 \times 0.147 \times 0.26)/(105 \times 0.344 \times 0.5) = 1$, $\mathrm{Bi}_1 = h\delta_1/k_1 = 0.8$, and $T = 0.775$. From the chart, $\mathrm{Fo}_1/(1/\mathrm{Bi}_1 + 1)(n + \frac{1}{2}) = 1.2$ whereby $\theta_{\mathrm{allow}} = 1.2(1/\mathrm{Bi}_1 + 1)(n + \frac{1}{2})\delta_1^2/\alpha_1 = 1.2(1/0.8 + 1)(1 + \frac{1}{2})(0.5/12)^2/0.000294 = 23.9$ sec. (*c*) For zirconia, $\rho = 175$ lb/ft³, $C = 0.156$ Btu/lb-°F and $k = 0.0000833$ Btu/sec-ft-°F, so $\alpha = 0.305 \times 10^{-5}$ ft²/sec. By comparison, graphite is a much better thermal conductor than zirconia (by two orders of magnitude) and as such the graphite may be considered as a simple capacitive heat sink ($k_2 \to \infty$). In this case Chart 30(*b*) applies with $n = (105 \times 0.344 \times 0.5)/(175 \times 0.156 \times 0.071) = 9.32$ and $\mathrm{Bi}_1 = 0.204(0.071/12)/0.0000833 = 14.5$. Then $\mu = n + (n + 1)/\mathrm{Bi}_1 = 9.32 + (9.32 + 1)/14.5 = 10$, and from the chart $\mathrm{Fo}_1 = 16 = \alpha_1\theta/\delta_1^2$ from which $\theta_{\mathrm{allow}} = 16(0.071/12)^2/0.305 \times 10^{-5} = 184$ sec.

EXAMPLE 4. A power transistor, used as a single-pulse output device, generates heat in a silicon junction, the heat being conducted into a 0.05″-thick copper heat-sink base (Fig. 7). With application of voltage, the heat rate developed increases linearly with time as $q = 600\theta$ Btu/sec-in² up to a pulse duration of 0.01 sec, and then decays suddenly to zero. Considering the device to be initially at 70°F and assuming the copper base to be perfectly insulated except at the heat-input surface, compute: (*a*) the peak temperatures of the two copper face surfaces, and (*b*) the equilibrium temperature of the base and the time required to reach this temperature after the pulse has ended.

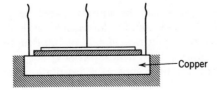

Fig. 7. Transistor.

Solution. The maximum heat input at $P = 0.01$ sec is $q_{max} = 6$ Btu/sec-in^2 = 864 Btu/sec-ft^2, and thus the total heat input is $Q = q_{max}P/2 = 864 \times 0.01/2 = 4.32$ Btu/ft^2. Under the condition of linearly increasing heat input, Chart 45 applies. (*a*) For copper $\rho = 558$ lb/ft^3, $C = 0.092$ Btu/lb-°F, and $k = 0.0623$ Btu/sec-ft-°F, so $\alpha = k/\rho C = 0.0623/558 \times 0.092 = 0.00122$ ft^2/sec. Then Fo' $= \alpha P/\delta^2 = 0.00122 \times 0.01/(0.05/12)^2 = 0.703$. The peak base temperatures occur at $\theta = P$. Using Chart 45(*a*) with $X = 0$ and Fo $= 0.703$ ($\theta = P$), the maximum temperature of the heated face is $T = 0.918 =$ Fo'$(kP/\delta Q) \times (t - t_0)$, or $t = 70 + 0.918(0.05/12)4.32/0.703 \times 0.0623 \times 0.01 = 70 + 37.8 = 108$°F. The maximum back face temperature at $X = 1$ is $T = 0.300$, or $t = 70 + 37.8 \times 0.300/0.918 = 82$°F. (*b*) The base equilibrium temperature is $T = ($Fo'$)^2 = (0.703)^2 = 0.494$, or $t = 70 + 37.8 \times 0.494/0.918 = 90$°F. If equilibrium is taken as 2% over 0.494, then for the heated surface $T = 0.494 \times 1.02 = 0.504$. Using Chart 45(*b*), this temperature occurs at Fo $= 1.03 = \alpha\theta/\delta^2$, or $\theta = 1.03(0.05/12)^2/0.00122 = 0.0147$ sec, approximated 0.005 sec after end of heating. For the insulated surface ($X = 1$), $T = 0.494 \times 0.98 = 0.484$ at 2% under equilibrium, and by Chart 45(*c*) Fo $= 1.10$ so $\theta = 0.0147 \times 1.10/1.03 = 0.0157$ sec, or approximately 0.006 sec after end of heating.

EXAMPLE 5. An analysis of the aerodynamic heating of a metallic heat-sink nose cone for re-entry through Earth's atmosphere results in the heating pulse shown as a solid curve in Fig. 8. The pulse represents a total heat input of 7500 Btu/ft^2 for a region of peak heating on the forward portion of the re-entry body. If the nose cone is made of beryllium (melting temperature 2400°F) 0.9″ thick in this region, calculate: (*a*) the maximum temperature of the beryllium outer face based on an initial re-entry temperature of 100°F, (*b*) the time during heating when this maximum temperature occurs, and (*c*) the back face beryllium temperature at this time.

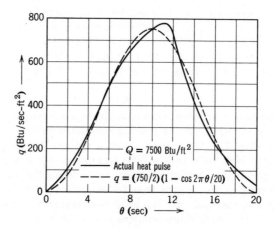

Fig. 8.   Re-entry heat input.

Solution. The heat pulse can be approximated as a cosine function $q = (q_{max}/2)(1 - \cos 2\pi\theta/P)$, as shown by the dashed curve in Fig. 8. The approximate pulse has a maximum heat rate of $q_{max} = 750$ Btu/sec-ft^2, a pulse period of $P = 20$ sec, and therefore a total heat input of $Q = q_{max}P/2 = 7500$ Btu/ft^2 as required. Considering the nose cone as a flat plate insulated at its back face,

Chart 47 applies. The average properties of beryllium at 1000°F are $\rho = 112$ lb/ft³, $C = 0.681$ Btu/lb-°F, and $k = 0.017$ Btu/sec-ft-°F, so $\alpha = k/\rho C = 0.017/112 \times 0.681 = 0.000223$ ft²/sec. (a) The modified Fourier number is $\mathrm{Fo}' = \alpha P/2\pi\delta^2 = 0.000223 \times 20/2 \times 3.14(0.9/12)^2 = 0.126$. From Chart 47(a), the maximum exposed surface temperature ($X = 0$) is $T_{max} = 4.75 = (k/\delta q_{max}\mathrm{Fo}')(t_{max} - t_0)$, or $t_{max} = 100 + 4.75(0.9/12)750 \times 0.126/0.017 = 100 + 1980 = 2080$°F. (b) From Chart 47(a), the maximum outer surface temperature for $\mathrm{Fo}' = 0.126$ occurs at $\mathrm{Fo}/\mathrm{Fo}' = 4.25 = 2\pi(\theta/P)$, or at $\theta = 4.25 \times 20/2 \times 3.14 = 13.5$ sec. (c) Using Chart 47(g) at $\mathrm{Fo}/\mathrm{Fo}' = 4.25$, the back face temperature at 13.5 sec is $T = 1.41$, or $t = 100 + 1980 \times 1.41/4.75 = 688$°F.

EXAMPLE 6. A hypersonic aircraft with 2″-thick solid aluminum wings is flying steadily at a Mach number of 1 at 50,000-ft altitude when its speed is suddenly increased by a constant acceleration at the same altitude to a Mach number of 7 within 2 minutes. During this acceleration period the unit surface conductance at a midchord station of the bottom wing surface increases linearly with time as $h = 25 + 4320\theta$ Btu/hr-ft²-°F, where θ is in hours. Calculate the wing surface temperature at this station during acceleration up to Mach number 7.

Solution. Consider the symmetrical wing modeled by a plate of semi-thickness $\delta = 1''$ (Fig. 9), and assume that the temperature potential $(t_a - t_e)$ increases linearly with time. Then, since h also increases linearly, Chart 49 applies as a special case with $i = 1$ and $j = 2$, giving the linear functions $\mathrm{Bi} = \mathrm{Bi}_0 + \mathrm{Bi}_1\mathrm{Fo}$ and $t_a - t_e = s\mathrm{Fo}$. Under these conditions the temperature response is $T = (t - t_0)/s\mathrm{Fo} = (t - t_0)/(t_a - t_e) = \mathrm{Bi}_0 Z_3 + \mathrm{Bi}_1\mathrm{Fo}Z_5$. For the surface

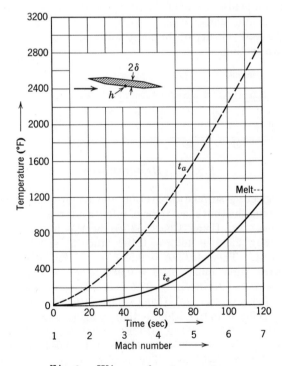

Fig. 9. *Wing surface temperature.*

temperature ($X = 0$), $t = t_e$ and the Z_3 and Z_5 are obtained from Chart 49(a). Once T_e is obtained, the surface temperature can be computed as $t_e = (t_0 + T_e t_a)/(1 + T_e)$. For aluminum, $\rho = 173$ lb/ft^3, $C = 0.230$ Btu/lb-°F and $k = 70.0$ Btu/hr-ft^2-°F, so $\alpha = 1.76$ ft^2/hr. The Biot number is Bi $= h\delta/k = 25(\delta/k) + 4320(\delta^3/k\alpha)$Fo $= 25(1/12 \times 70.0) + 4320(1/1728 \times 70.0 \times 1.76)$Fo $= 0.02977 + 0.02030$Fo, and the Fourier number is Fo $= \alpha\theta/\delta^2 = (1.76 \times 144/1 \times 3600)\theta = 0.0704\theta$ (sec). The adiabatic wall (recovery) temperature t_a of the high-speed flow is calculated with a recovery factor of 0.9 and the properties of air at 50,000-ft altitude. The initial temperature at 50,000 ft and steady flight at a Mach number of 1 is approximately $t_0 = 0$°F. The calculations of surface temperature history t_e are tabulated below and plotted in Fig. 9.

θ (sec)	t_a(°F)	Fo	Z_3	Z_5	T_e	t_e(°F)
20	210	1.408	1.020	0.775	0.0525	11
40	540	2.816	1.740	1.240	0.1226	59
60	1008	4.224	2.450	1.715	0.2200	182
80	1578	5.632	3.170	2.200	0.3459	405
100	2221	7.040	3.810	2.625	0.4887	729
120	2940	8.448	4.500	3.120	0.6684	1178

EXAMPLE 7. A continuous sheet of 0.041″-thick metal alloy of density 486 lb/ft^3 and specific heat 0.11 Btu/lb-°F is heat treated by passing it at constant velocity through a radiant oven designed to provide a rapid heat-up and cool-down cycle. The oven consists of a 10′-long ceiling heat source section ($F_A F_\epsilon = 0.72$) maintained at 2200°F followed by a ceiling heat-sink section ($F_A F_\epsilon = 0.86$) maintained at −200°F (Fig. 10). If the sheet stock enters the oven at 70°F and must be heated to 2000°F and cooled down to at least 500°F before leaving the oven and slowly cooling to room temperature in air, calculate: (a) the required feed velocity of the sheet material, and (b) the required length of the cool-down section.

Heating   Cooling

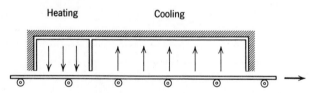

Fig. 10.   Heat-treat oven.

Solution. Neglecting surface convection and longitudinal conduction in the sheet, and assuming the thin sheet to be of infinite internal thermal conductance, Chart 53 applies. (a) Using Chart 53(a) for the heating section, $1/T_s = t_0/t_s = (70 + 460)/(2200 + 460) = 0.199$ and $T = t/t_0 = (2000 + 460)/(70 + 460) = 4.64$. Then MT_s^3Fo $= 0.980 = (\sigma F_A F_\epsilon t_s^3/\rho C\delta)\theta$, from which the heat-up exposure time must be $\theta = 0.980 \times 486 \times 0.11(0.041/12)/17.3 \times 10^{-10} \times 0.72(2660)^3 = 0.00764$ hr $= 27.5$ sec. The required feed velocity is thus $10/27.5 = 0.364$ ft/sec. (b) Using Chart 53(b) for the cool-down section, $1/T_s = t_0/t_s = (2000 + 460)/(-200 + 460) = 9.46$ and $T = t/t_0 = (500 + 460)/(2000 + 460) = 0.39$. Then MT_s^3Fo $= 0.0064$ and the required cool-down exposure time is $\theta = 0.0064 \times 486 \times 0.11(0.041/12)/17.3 \times 10^{-10} \times 0.86(260)^3 = 0.0448$ hr $= 161$ sec. The required length of cool-down section is therefore $0.364 \times 161 = 59$ ft.

6

List of Charts

*Italicized numbers in parentheses refer to the References on page 151.

7

Charts

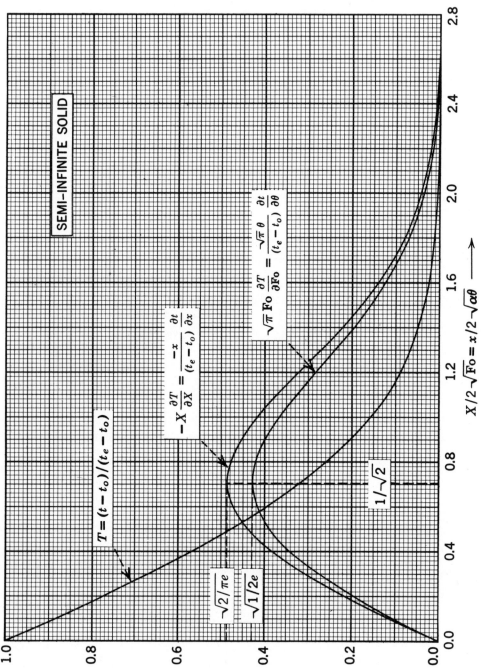

Chart 1. Temperature response, temperature gradient and heating rate in a semi-infinite solid, $x \geq 0$, after sudden change in surface temperature from t_0 when $\theta < 0$ to t_e for $\theta \geq 0$, (E).*

*Italicized letters in parentheses indicate whether curves are based on exact, integral or numerical solutions.

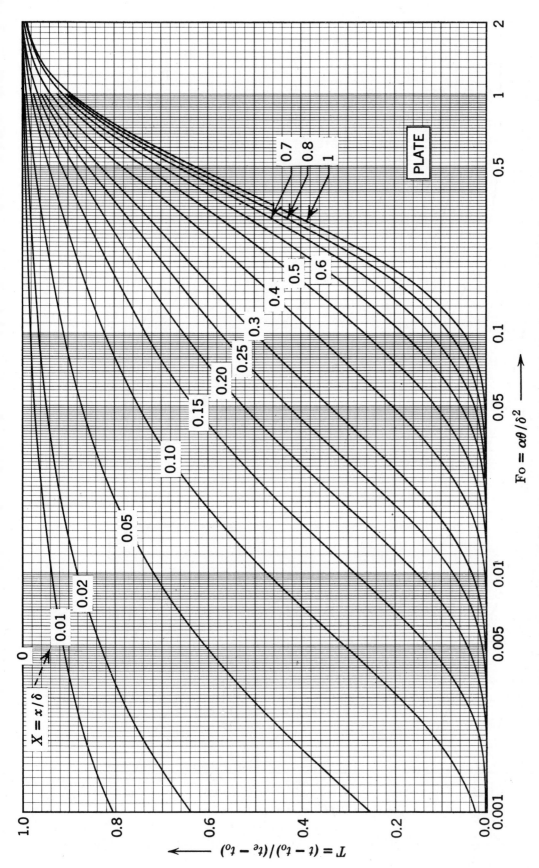

Chart 2. Temperature response of a plate, $0 \leq x \leq \delta$, with insulated back face $x = \delta$ after sudden change in external surface temperature at $x = 0$ from t_0 when $\theta < 0$ to t_e for $\theta \geq 0$, (E).

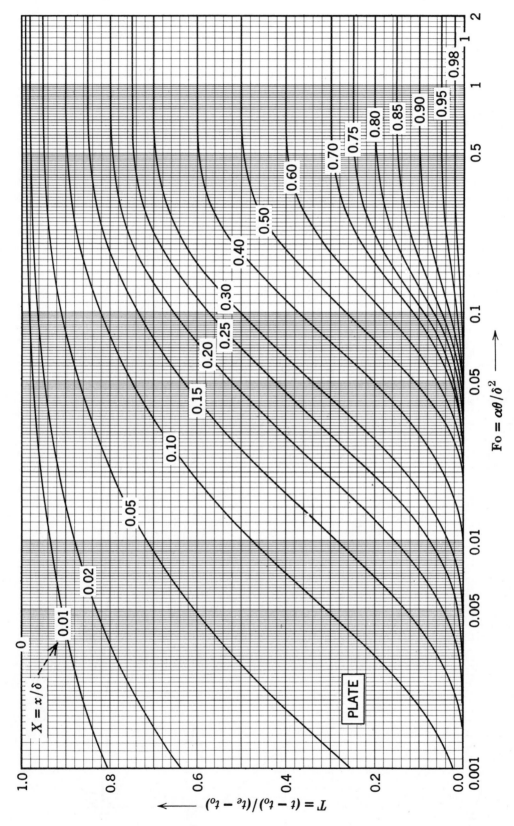

Chart 3. Temperature response of a plate, $0 \leq x \leq \delta$, with back face $x = \delta$ maintained at t_0 after sudden change in external surface temperature at $x = 0$ from t_0 when $\theta < 0$ to t_e for $\theta \geq 0$, (E).

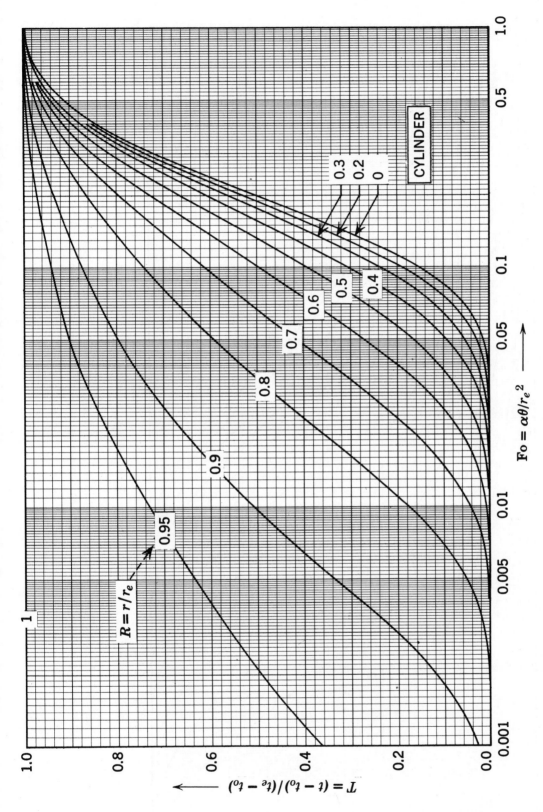

Chart 4. Temperature response of a cylinder, $0 \leq r \leq r_e$, after sudden change in external surface temperature at $r = r_e$ from t_0 when $\theta < 0$ to t_e for $\theta \geq 0$, (E).

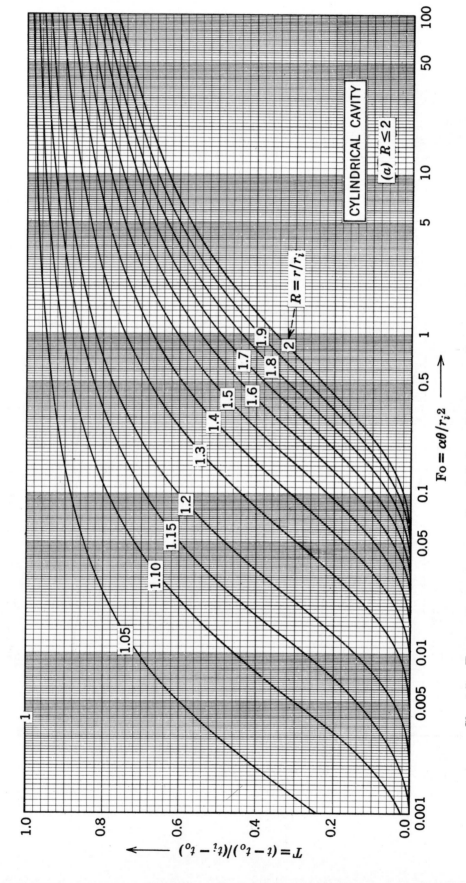

Chart 5. Temperature response of an infinite solid surrounding a cylindrical cavity, $r \geq r_i$, after sudden change in internal surface temperature at $r = r_i$ from t_0 when $\theta < 0$ to t_i for $\theta \geq 0$; (a) $R \leq 2$, (N, E) (*Continued*).

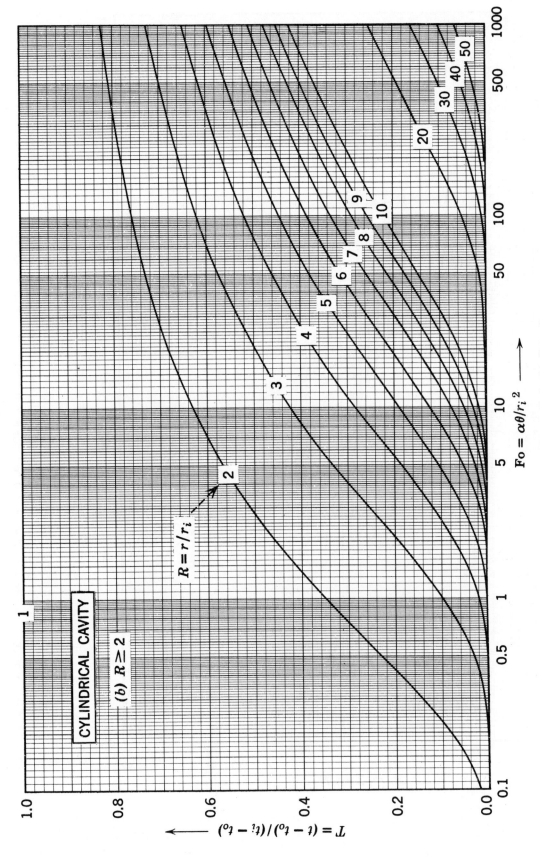

Chart 5. *Concluded;* (b) $R \geq 2$.

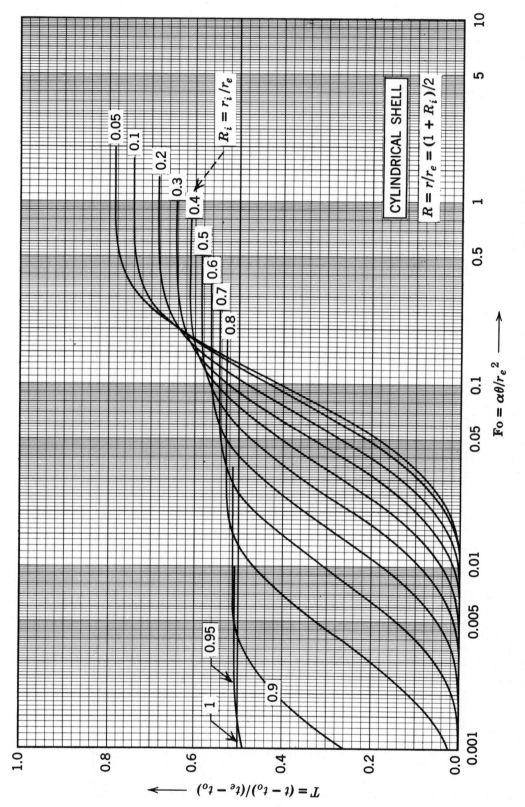

Chart 6. Temperature response at midplane of a cylindrical shell, $r_i \leq r \leq r_e$, with internal surface temperature at $r = r_i$ maintained at t_0 after sudden change in external surface temperature at $r = r_e$ from t_0 when $\theta < 0$ to t_e for $\theta \geq 0$, (E).

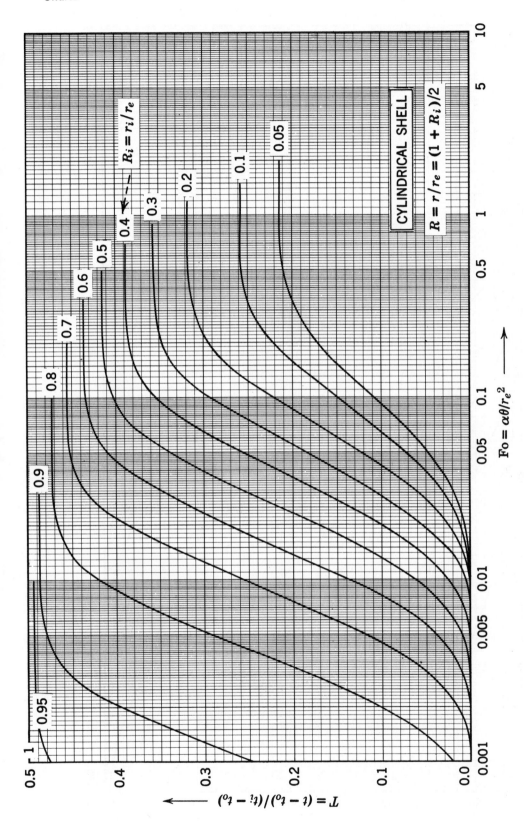

Chart 7. Temperature response at midplane of a cylindrical shell, $r_i \leq r \leq r_e$, with external surface temperature at $r = r_e$ maintained at t_0 after sudden change in internal surface temperature at $r = r_i$ from t_0 when $\theta < 0$ to t_i for $\theta \geq 0$, (E).

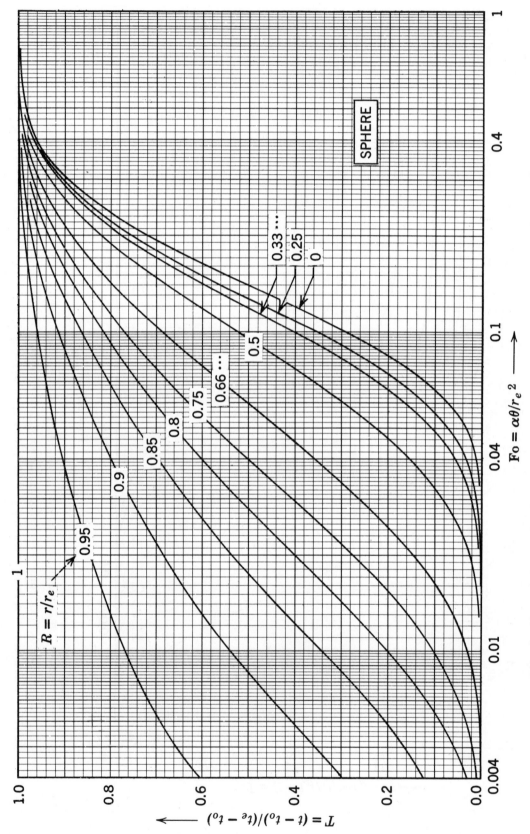

Chart 8. Temperature response of a sphere, $0 \le r \le r_e$, after sudden change in external surface temperature at $r = r_e$ from t_0 when $\theta < 0$ to t_e for $\theta \ge 0$, (E, E).

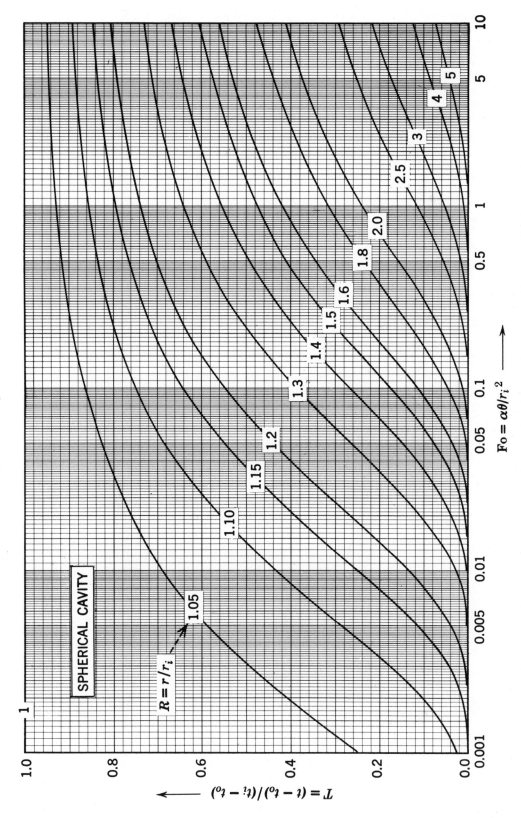

Chart 9. Temperature response of an infinite solid surrounding a spherical cavity, $r \geq r_i$, after sudden change in internal surface temperature at $r = r_i$ from t_0 when $\theta < 0$ to t_i for $\theta \geq 0$, (E).

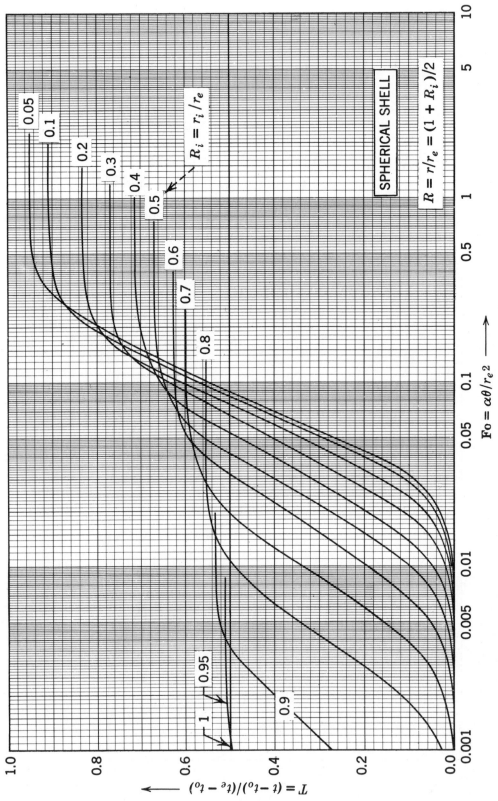

Chart 10. Temperature response at midplane of a spherical shell, $r_i \leq r \leq r_e$, with internal surface temperature at $r = r_i$ maintained at t_0 after sudden change in external surface temperature at $r = r_e$ from t_0 when $\theta < 0$ to t_e for $\theta \geq 0$, (E).

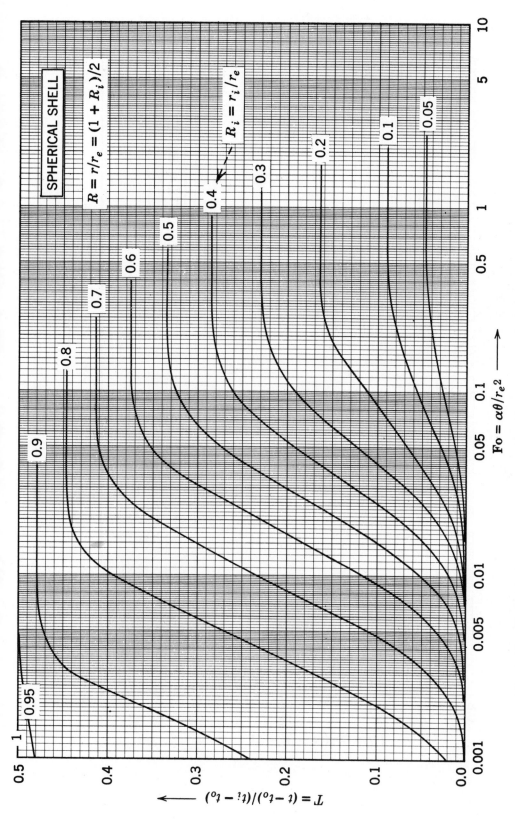

Chart 11. Temperature response at midplane of a spherical shell, $r_i \leq r \leq r_e$, with external surface temperature at $r = r_e$ maintained at t_0 after sudden change in internal surface temperature at $r = r_i$ from t_0 when $\theta < 0$, to t_i for $\theta \geq 0$, (E).

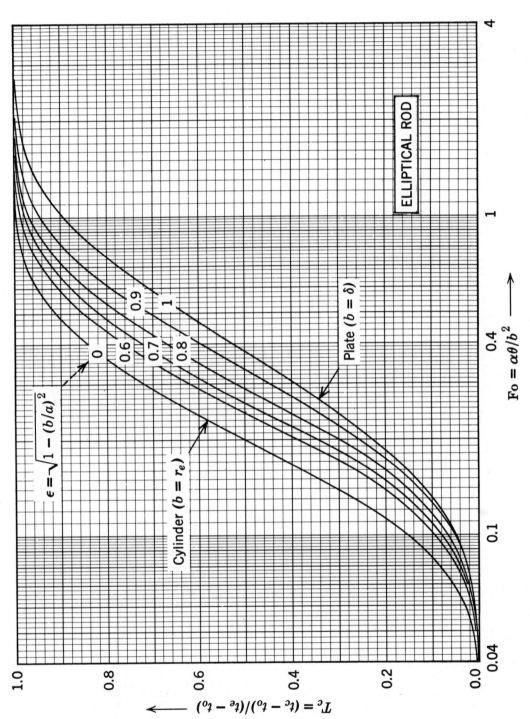

Chart 12. Temperature response at center of an elliptical rod of eccentricity ϵ after sudden change in external surface temperature from t_0 to t_e for $\theta \geq 0$, (E).

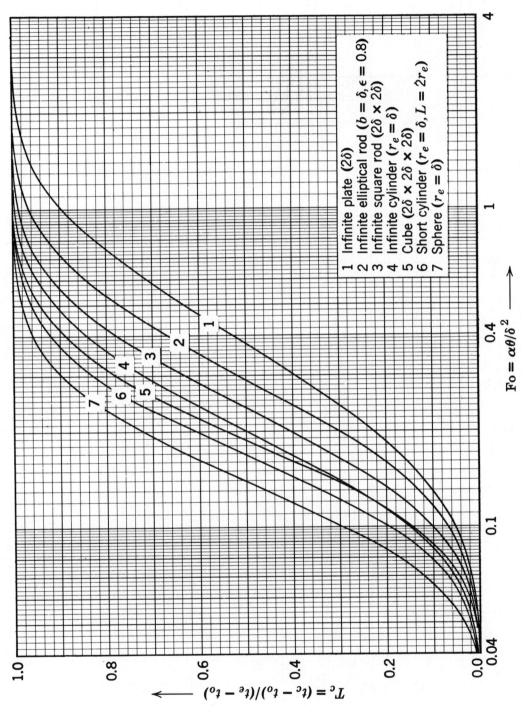

Chart 13. Temperature response at center of various body shapes after sudden change in external surface temperature from t_0 when $\theta < 0$ to t_e for $\theta \geq 0$, (E).

Legend (in chart):

1 Infinite plate (2δ)
2 Infinite elliptical rod $(b = \delta, \epsilon = 0.8)$
3 Infinite square rod $(2\delta \times 2\delta)$
4 Infinite cylinder $(r_e = \delta)$
5 Cube $(2\delta \times 2\delta \times 2\delta)$
6 Short cylinder $(r_e = \delta, L = 2r_e)$
7 Sphere $(r_e = \delta)$

Axes:

$Fo = \alpha\theta/\delta^2 \longrightarrow$

$\longleftarrow T_c = (t_c - t_0)/(t_e - t_0)$

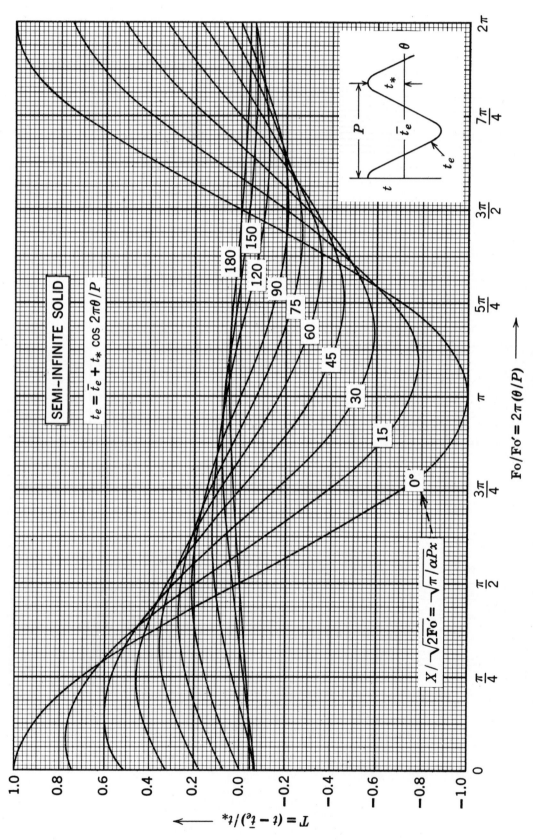

Chart 14. Temperature response of a semi-infinite solid, $x \geq 0$, with constant harmonic surface temperature variation t_e at $x = 0$ of amplitude t_* and period P, (E).

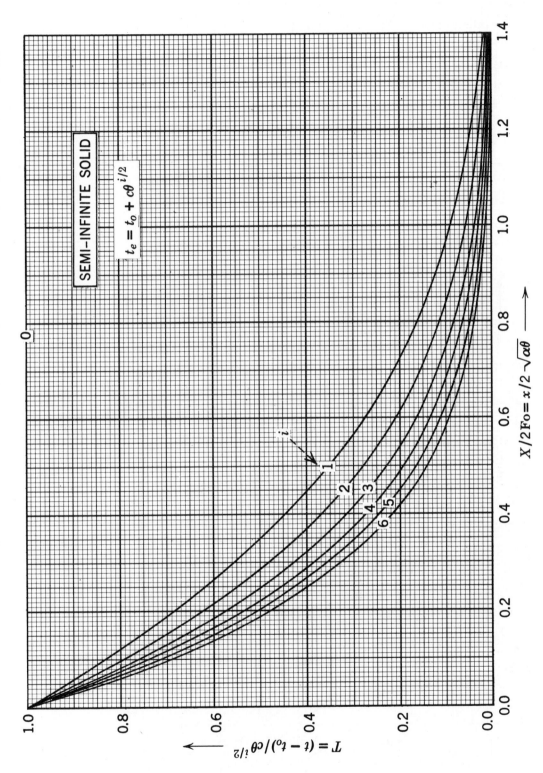

Chart 15. Temperature response of a semi-infinite solid, $x \geq 0$, with surface temperature variations at $x = 0$ between the square root and cube of time, (E).

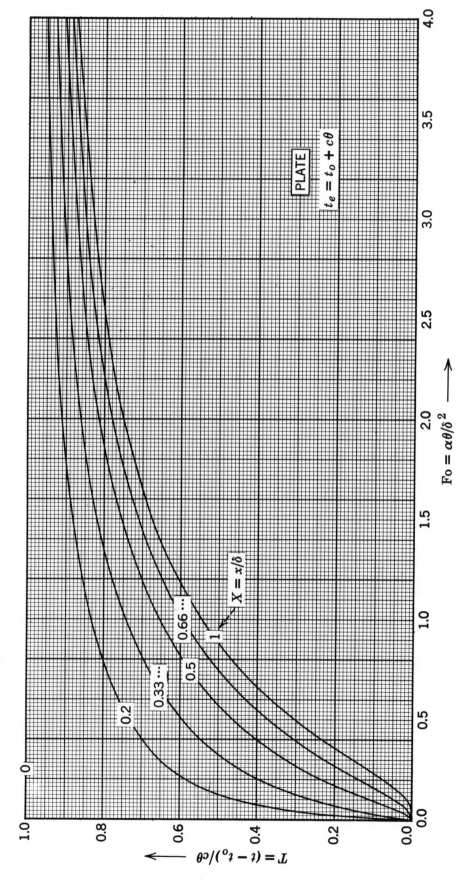

Chart 16. Temperature response of a plate, $0 \leq x \leq \delta$, with insulated back face $x = \delta$ and an external surface temperature at $x = 0$ varying linearly with time, (E).

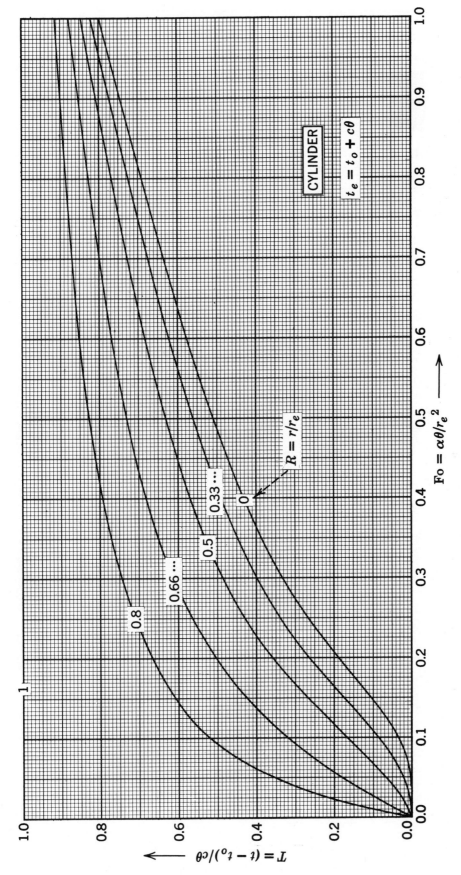

Chart 17. Temperature response of a cylinder, $0 \leq r \leq r_e$, with an external surface temperature at $r = r_e$ varying linearly with time, (E).

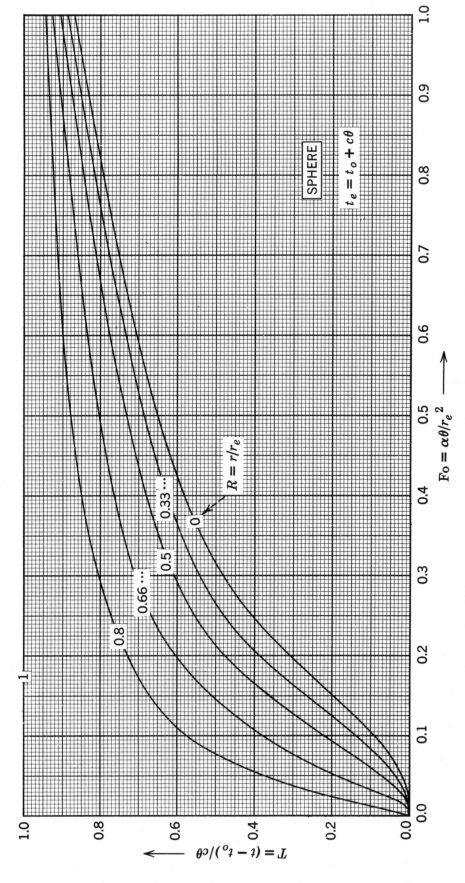

Chart 18. Temperature response of a sphere, $0 \leq r \leq r_e$, with an external surface temperature at $r = r_e$ varying linearly with time, (E).

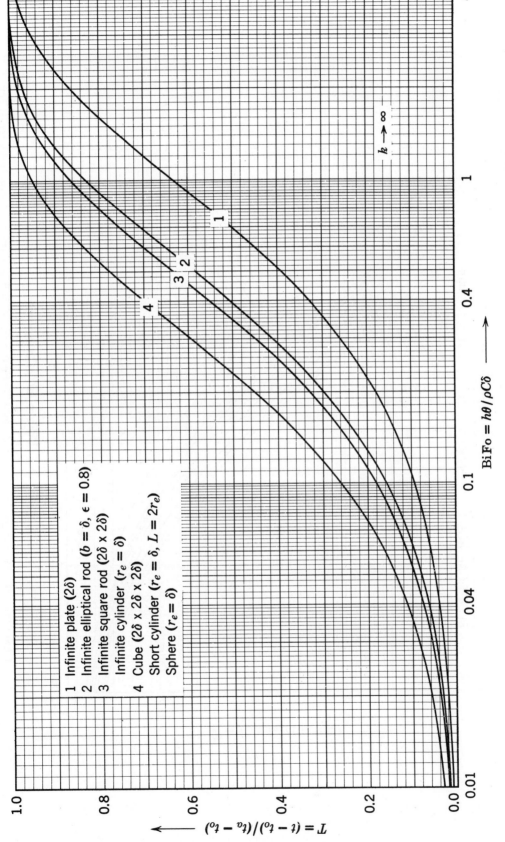

Chart 19. Temperature response of various body shapes of infinite internal conductance after sudden exposure to a uniform-temperature convective environment t_a, (E).

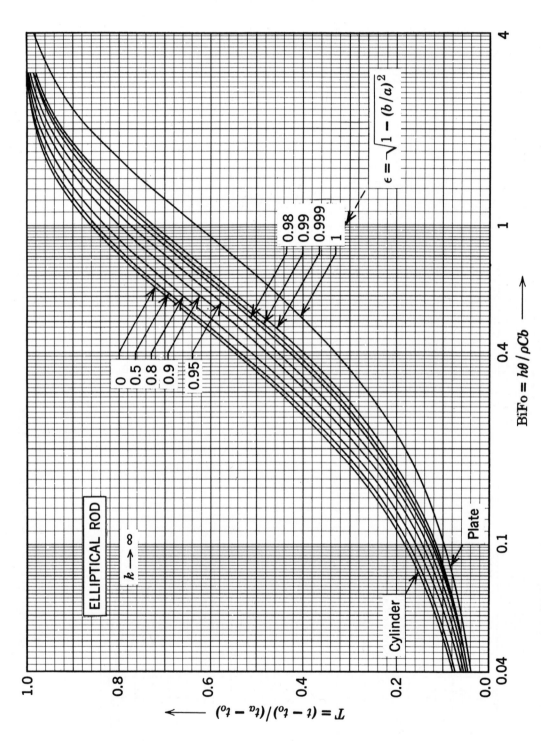

Chart 20. Temperature response of an elliptical rod of infinite internal conductance after sudden exposure to a uniform-temperature convective environment t_a, (E).

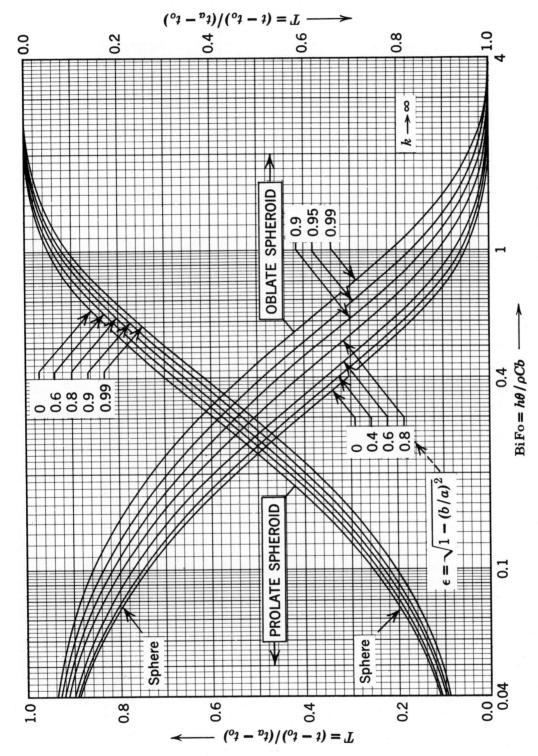

Chart 21. Temperature response of prolate and oblate spheroids of infinite internal conductance after sudden exposure to a uniform-temperature convective environment t_a, (E).

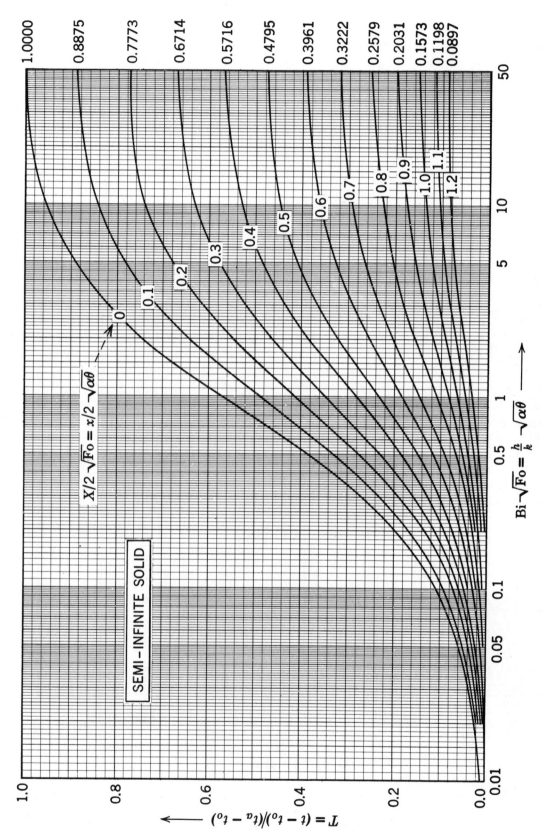

Chart 22. Temperature response of a semi-infinite solid, $x \geq 0$, after sudden exposure to a uniform-temperature convective environment t_a, (E).

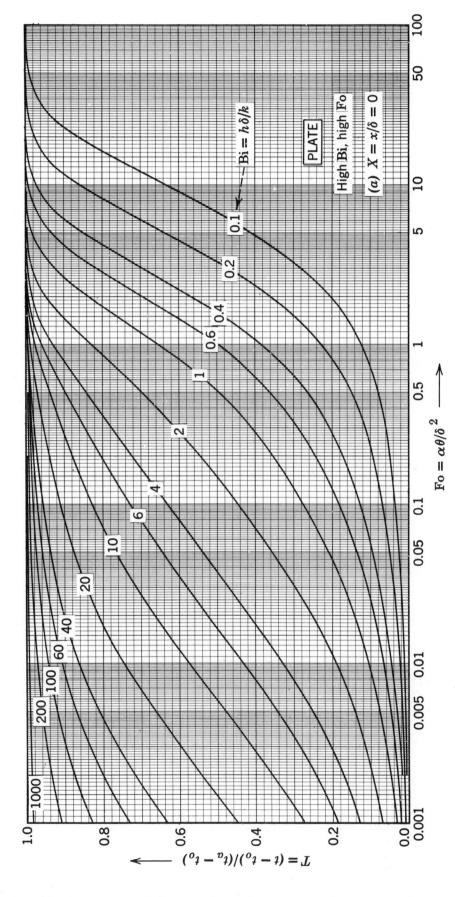

Chart 23. Temperature response of a plate, $0 \le x \le \delta$, with insulated back face $x = \delta$ after sudden exposure to a uniform-temperature convective environment t_a at $x = 0$; high Bi and high Fo; (a) $X = 0$, (E) (*Continued*).

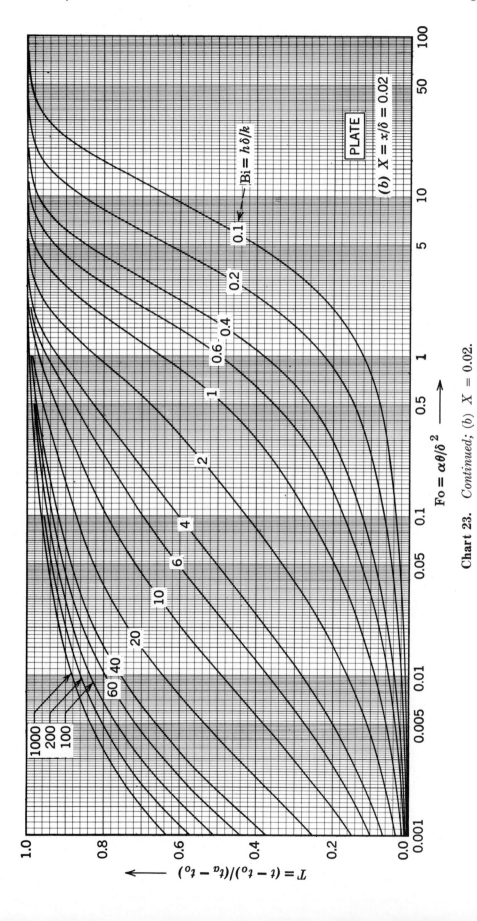

Chart 23. *Continued;* (b) X = 0.02.

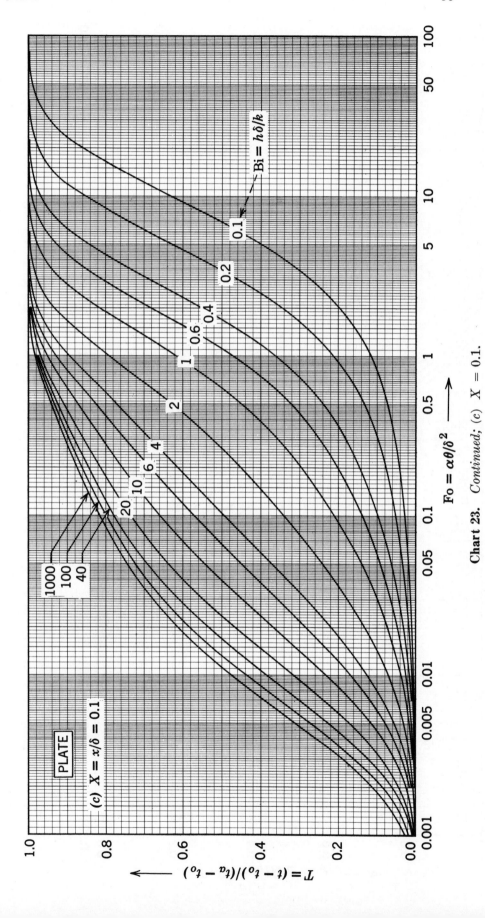

Chart 23. *Continued; (c) X = 0.1.*

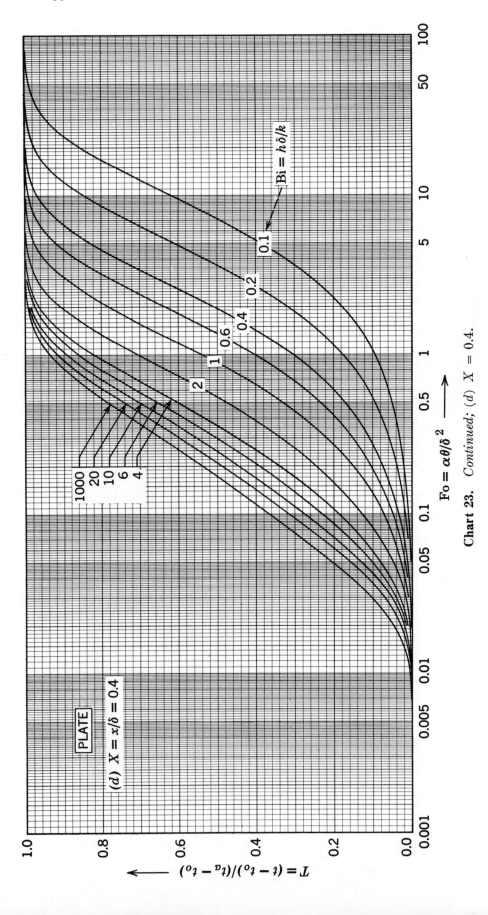

Chart 23. *Continued;* (*d*) $X = 0.4$.

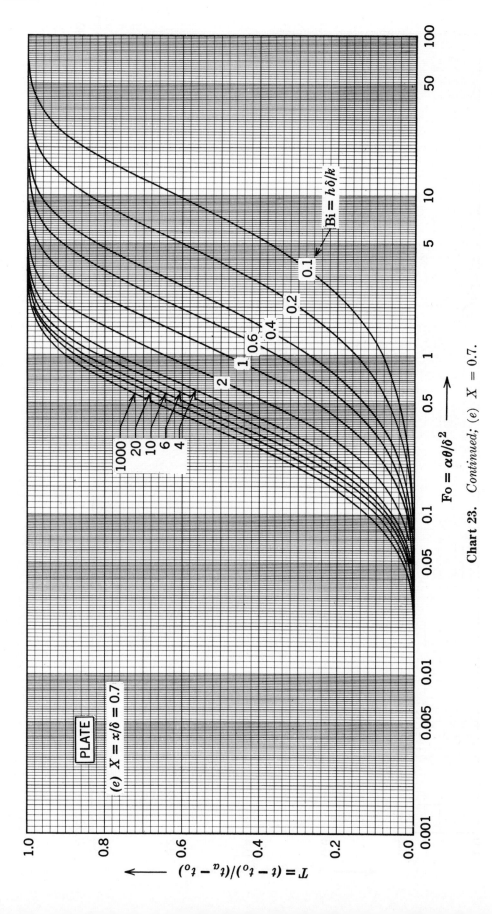

Chart 23. *Continued; (e)* $X = 0.7$.

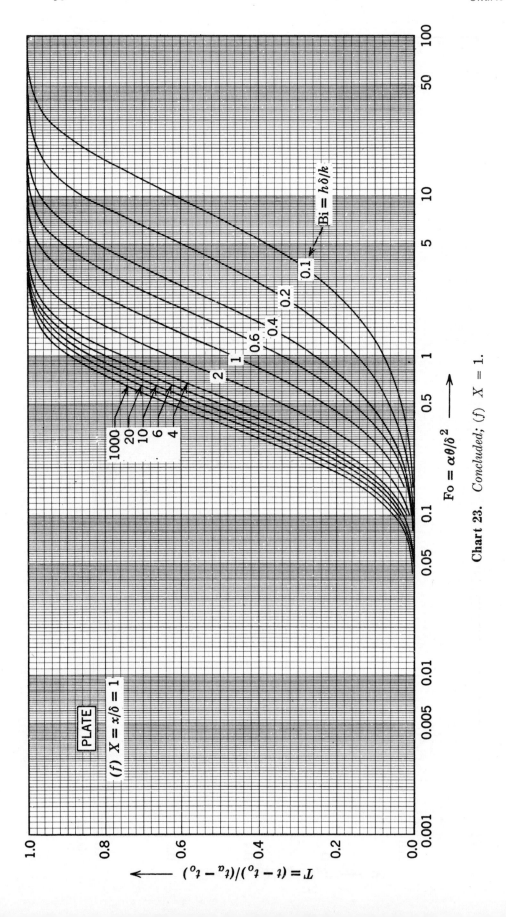

Chart 23. *Concluded;* (f) $X = 1$.

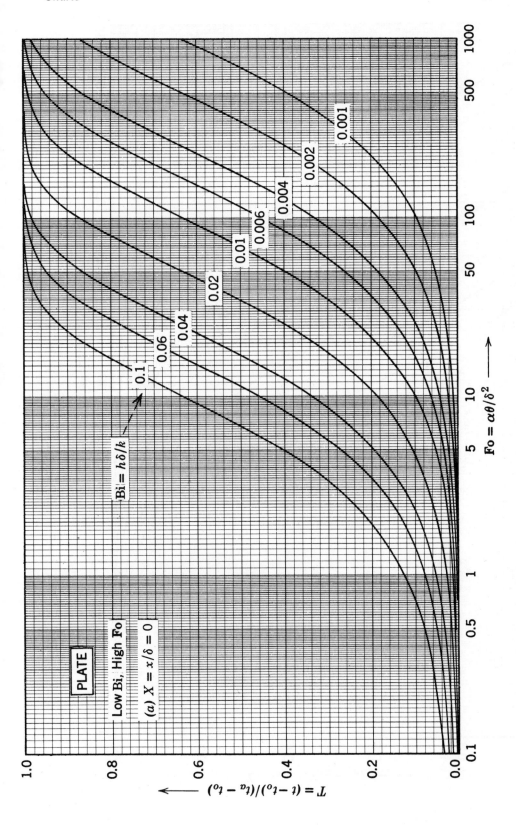

Chart 24. Temperature response of a plate, $0 \leq x \leq \delta$, with insulated back face $x = \delta$ after sudden exposure to a uniform-temperature convective environment t_a at $x = 0$: low Bi and high Fo; (*a*) $X = 0$, (*E*) (*Continued*).

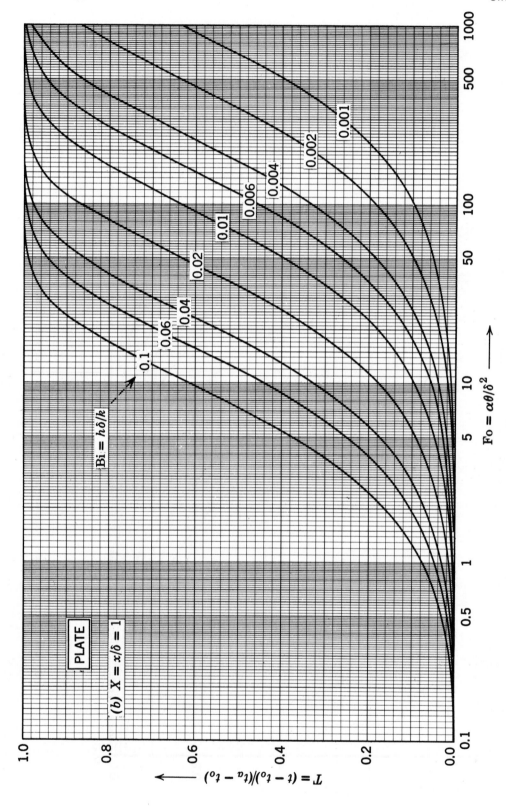

Chart 24. *Concluded; (b)* $X = 1$.

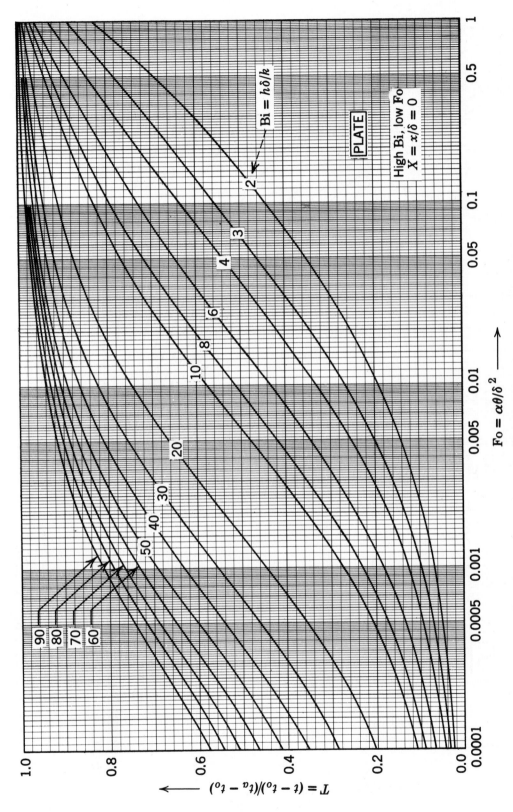

Chart 25. Temperature response of the front face of a plate, $0 \le x \le \delta$, with insulated back face $x = \delta$ after sudden exposure to a uniform-temperature convective environment t_a at $x = 0$: high Bi and low Fo, (E).

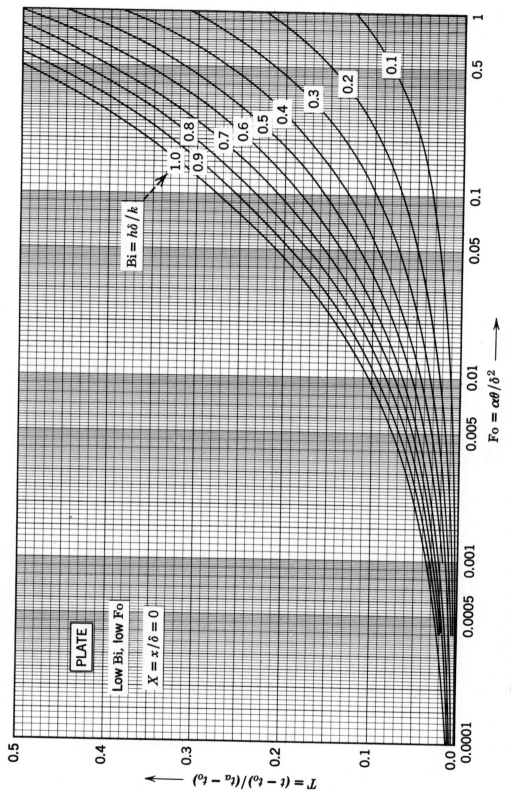

Chart 26. Temperature response of the front face of a plate, $0 \leq x \leq \delta$, with insulated back face $x = \delta$ after sudden exposure to a uniform-temperature convective environment t_a at $x = 0$: low Bi and low Fo, (E).

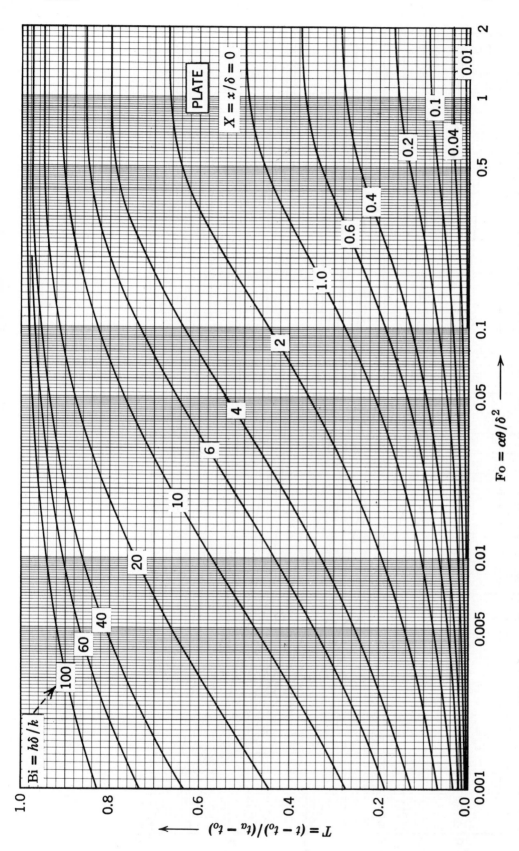

Chart 27. Temperature response of the front face of a plate, $0 \leq x \leq \delta$, with back face $x = \delta$ maintained at t_0 after sudden exposure to a uniform-temperature convective environment t_a at $x = 0$, (E).

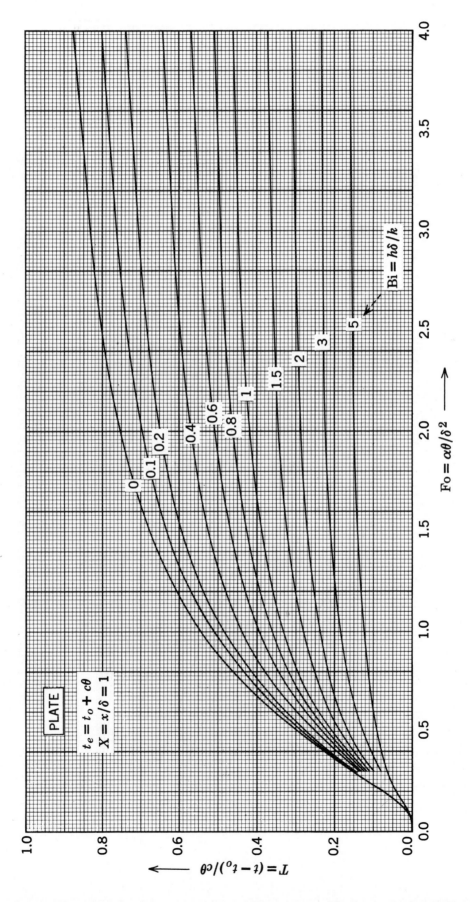

Chart 28. Temperature response of the back face of a plate, $0 \leq x \leq \delta$, with the back face $x = \delta$ exposed to a convective environment at t_0 ($= t_a$) and with the temperature of the front face at $x = 0$ varying linearly with time, (E).

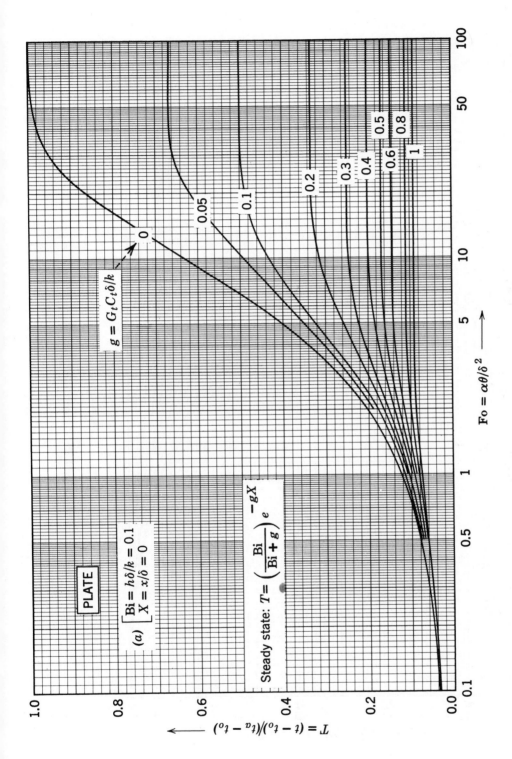

Chart 29. Temperature response of a porous plate, $0 \leq x \leq \delta$, after sudden exposure to a uniform-temperature convective environment t_a at $x = 0$ and cooled by a steady flow of transpiration fluid through the plate entering at $x = \delta$ with $t_i = t_0$ at $x \gg \delta$; (a) Bi = 0.1, $X = 0$, (E) (*Continued*).

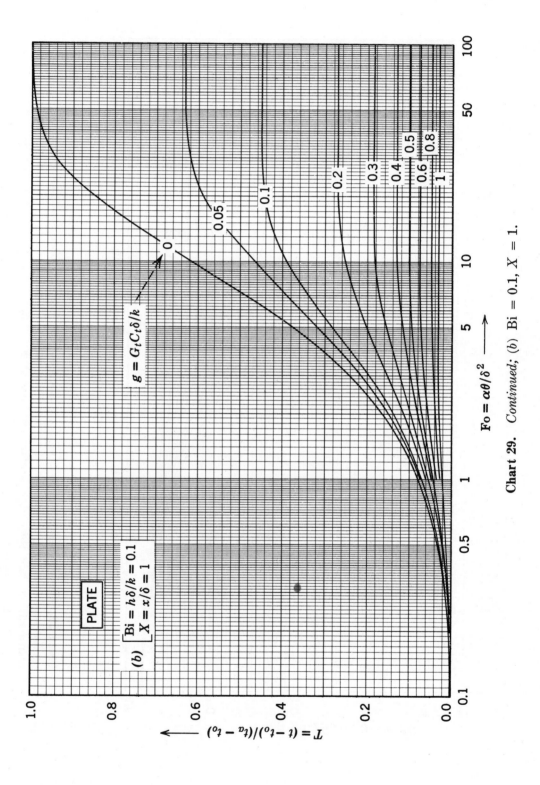

Chart 29. *Continued;* (b) Bi = 0.1, X = 1.

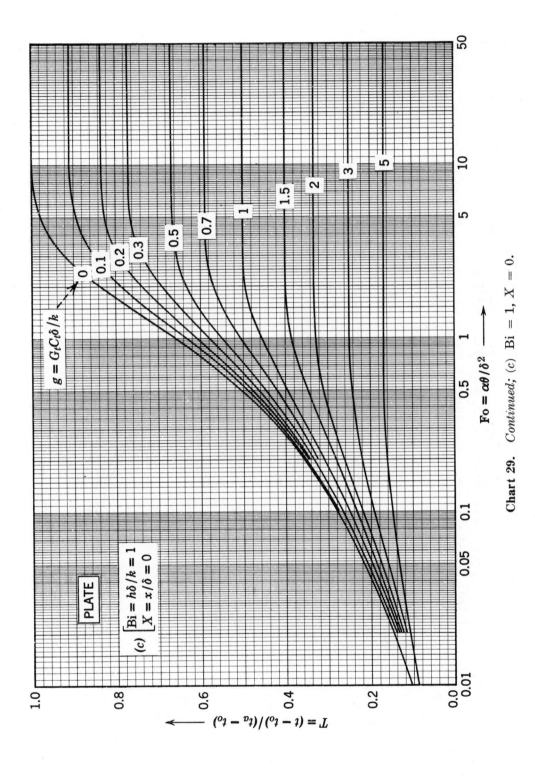

Chart 29. *Continued;* (c) Bi = 1, X = 0.

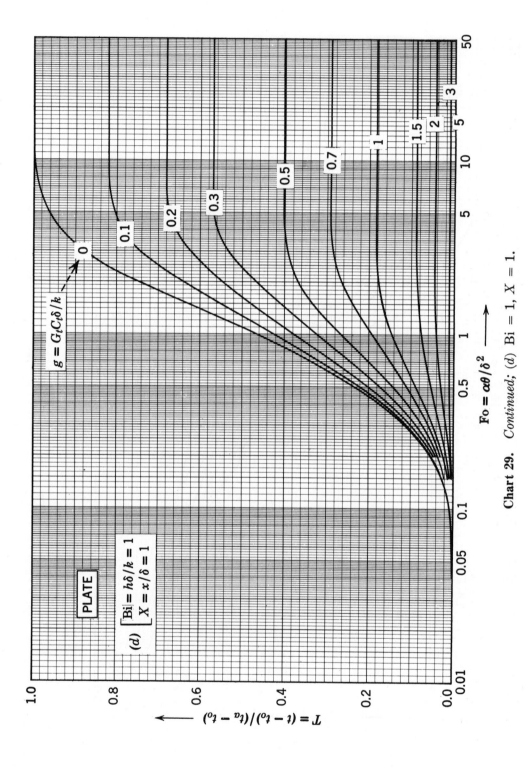

Chart 29. *Continued;* (d) Bi = 1, X = 1.

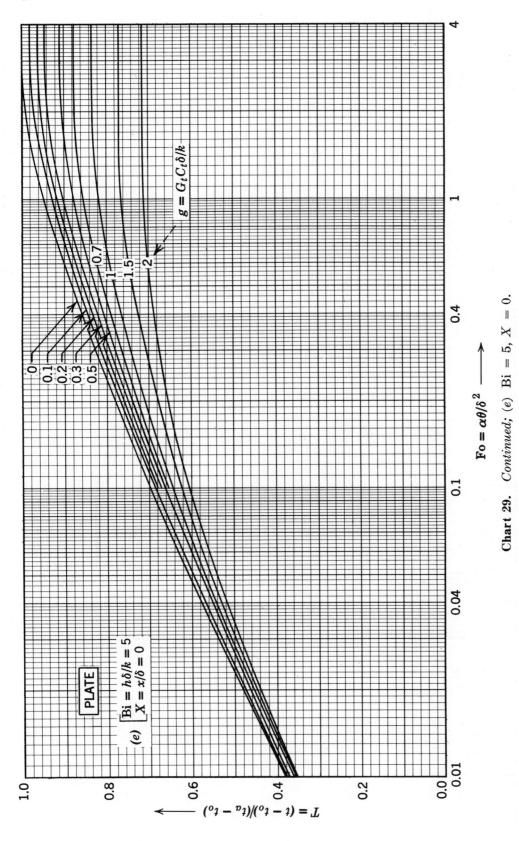

Chart 29. *Continued;* (e) Bi = 5, X = 0.

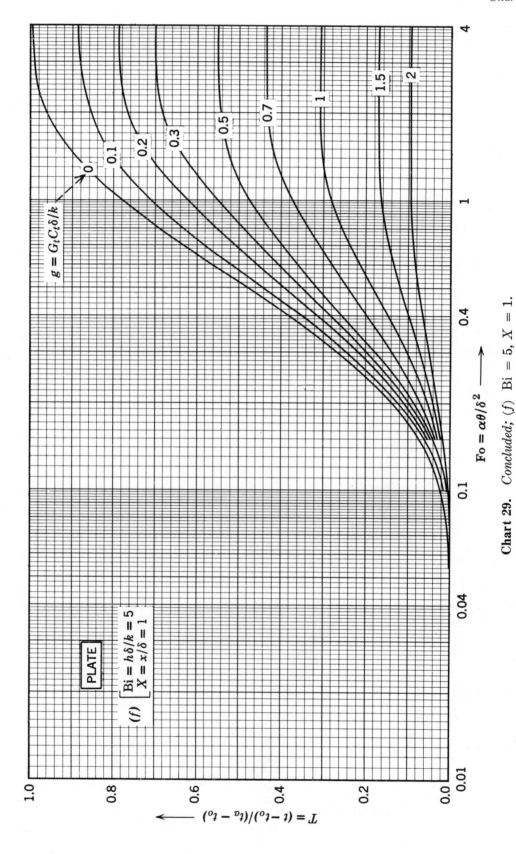

Chart 29. *Concluded;* (*f*) Bi = 5, X = 1.

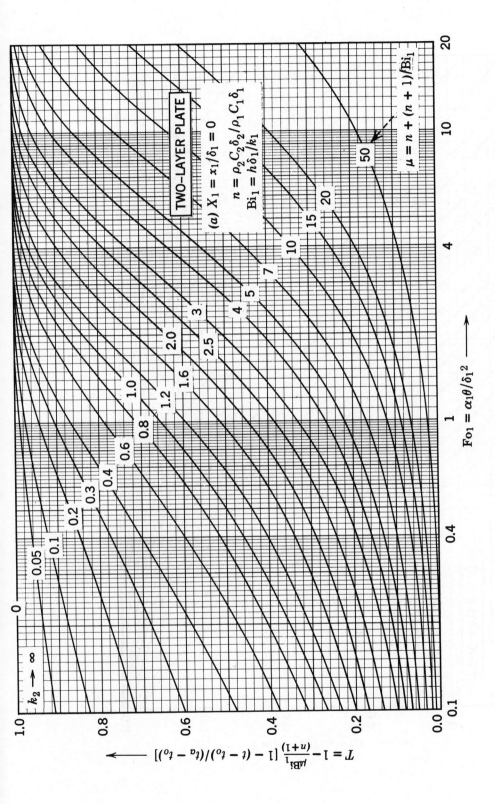

Chart 30. Temperature response of the front layer of a two-layer plate, $0 \leq x_1 \leq \delta_1$ and $0 \leq x_2 \leq \delta_2$, with back layer insulated at $x_2 = \delta_2$ and of infinite internal conductance after sudden exposure to a uniform-temperature convective environment t_a at $x_1 = 0$; (a) $X_1 = 0$, (E) (*Continued*).

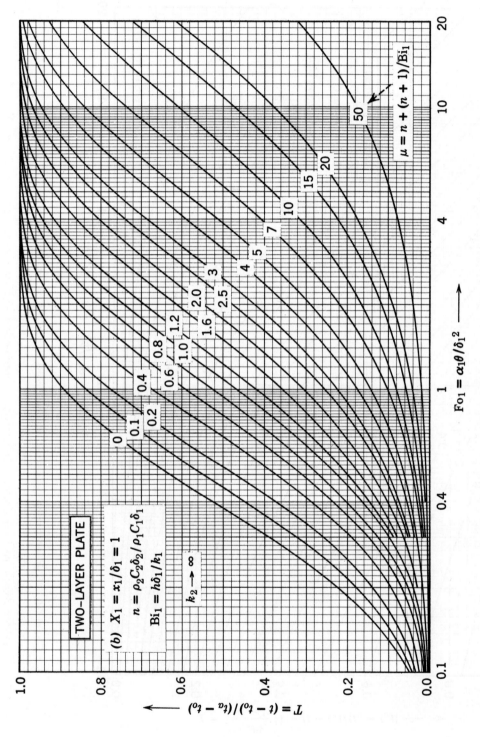

Chart 30. *Concluded; (b) $X_1 = 1$, $0 \leq X_2 \leq 1$, (E).*

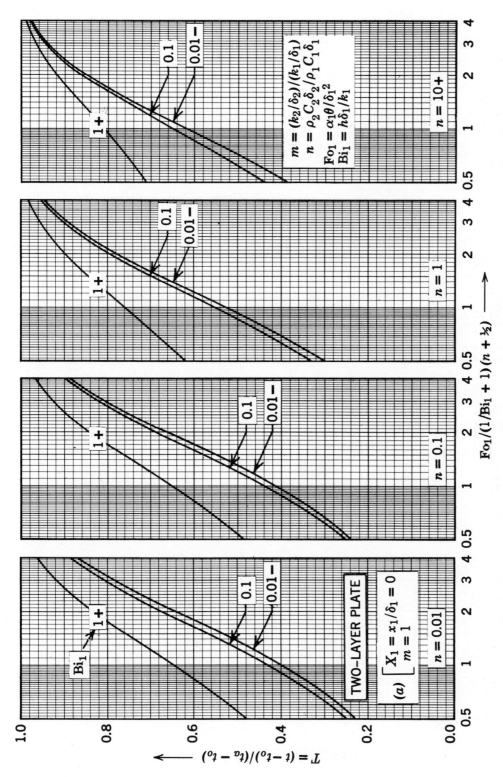

Chart 31. Temperature response of a two-layer plate, $0 \le x_1 \le \delta_1$ and $0 \le x_2 \le \delta_2$, with back layer insulated at $x_2 = \delta_2$ after sudden exposure to a uniform-temperature convective environment t_a at $x_1 = 0$ ($m \ge 1$); (a) $X_1 = 0$, $m = 1$, (E) (Continued).

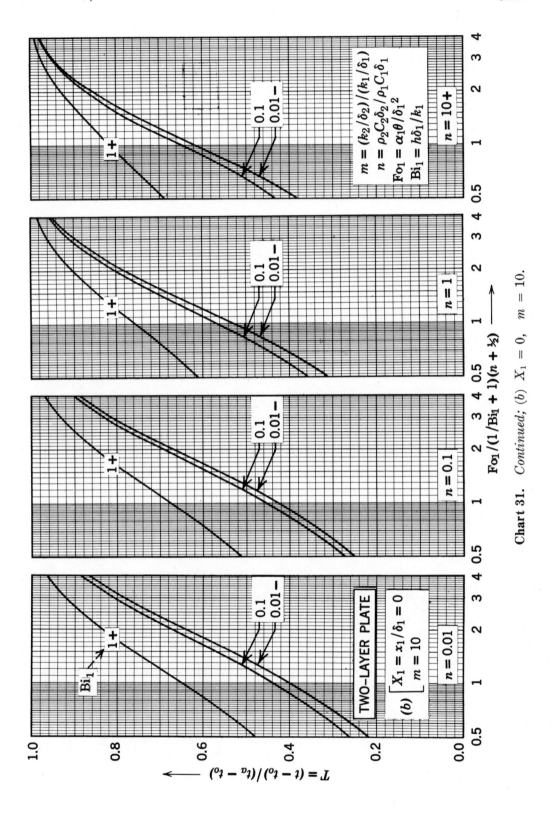

Chart 31. *Continued;* (b) $X_1 = 0$, $m = 10$.

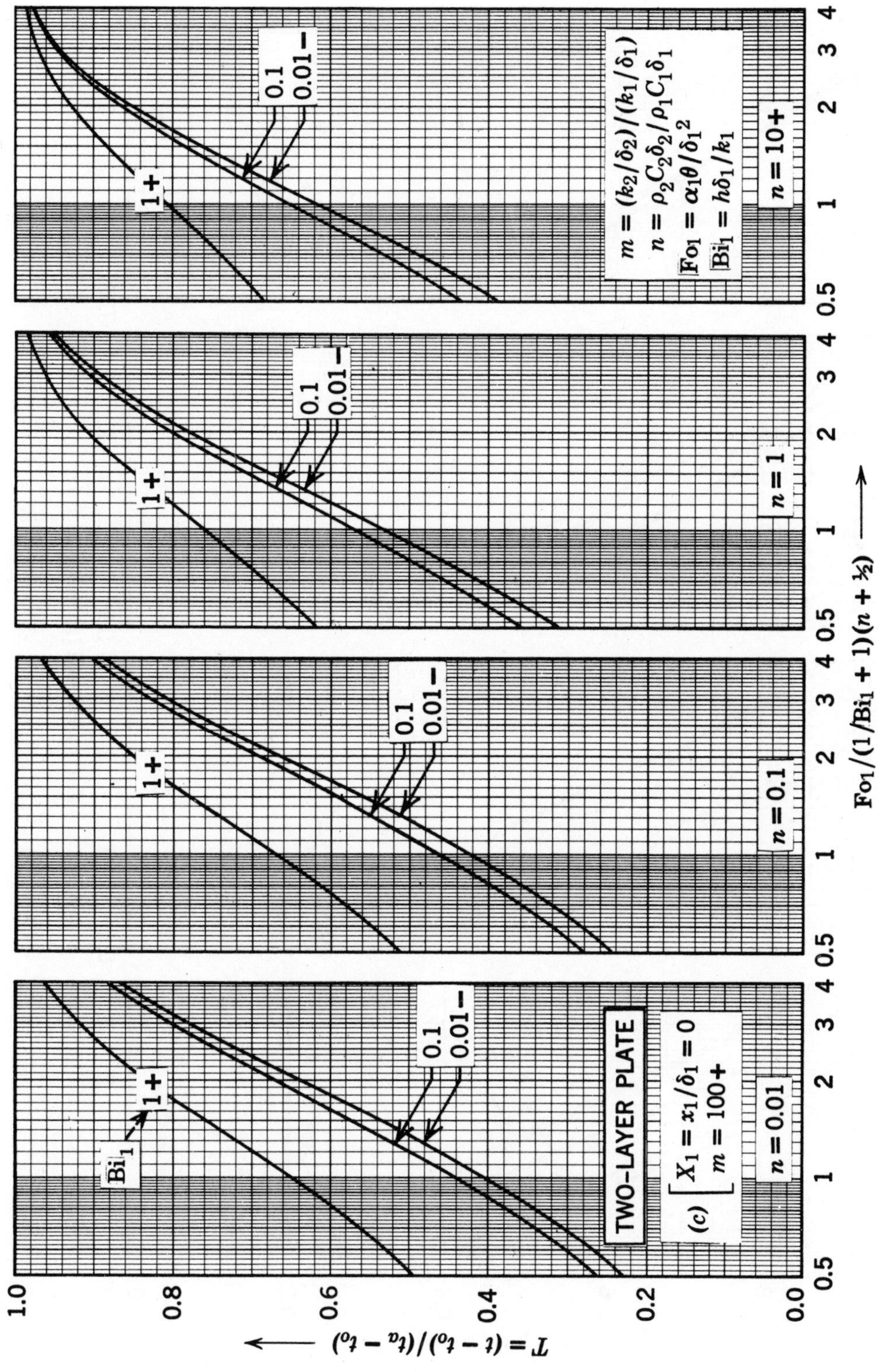
TWO-LAYER PLATE
(c) $X_1 = x_1/\delta_1 = 0$, $m = 100+$
$m = (k_2/\delta_2)/(k_1/\delta_1)$
$n = \rho_2 C_2 \delta_2/\rho_1 C_1 \delta_1$
$Fo_1 = \alpha_1 \theta/\delta_1^2$
$Bi_1 = h\delta_1/k_1$
Bi_1
1+
0.1
0.01−
n = 0.01
n = 0.1
n = 1
n = 10+
$T = (t - t_o)/(t_a - t_o)$
$Fo_1/(1/Bi_1 + 1)(n + \frac{1}{2})$
0.0
0.2
0.4
0.6
0.8
1.0
0.5
1
2
3
4

Chart 31. *Continued;* (c) $X_1 = 0$, $m = 100+$.

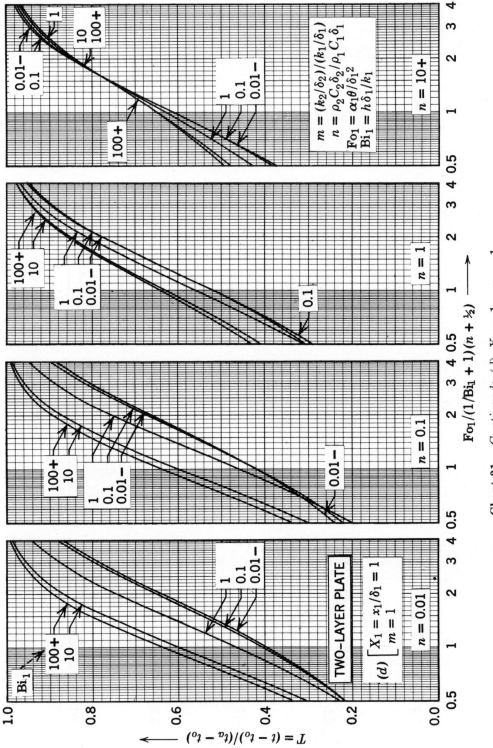

Chart 31. *Continued;* (*d*) $X_1 = 1$, $m = 1$.

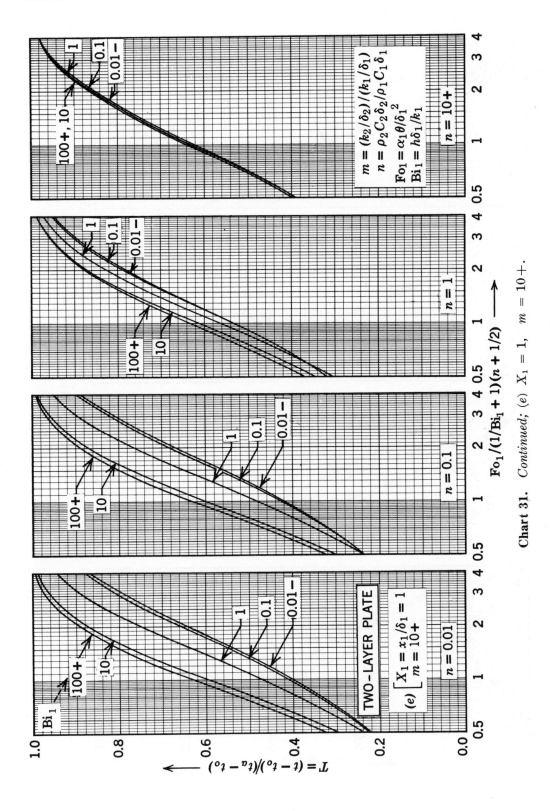

$$m = (k_2/\delta_2)/(k_1/\delta_1)$$
$$n = \rho_2 C_2 \delta_2/\rho_1 C_1 \delta_1$$
$$Fo_1 = \alpha_1 \theta/\delta_1^2$$
$$Bi_1 = h\delta_1/k_1$$

TWO-LAYER PLATE

$$(e) \begin{bmatrix} X_1 = x_1/\delta_1 = 1 \\ m = 10+ \end{bmatrix}$$

$$T = (t - t_o)/(t_a - t_o)$$

$$Fo_1/(1/Bi_1 + 1)(n + 1/2) \longrightarrow$$

Chart 31. *Continued;* (e) $X_1 = 1$, $m = 10+$.

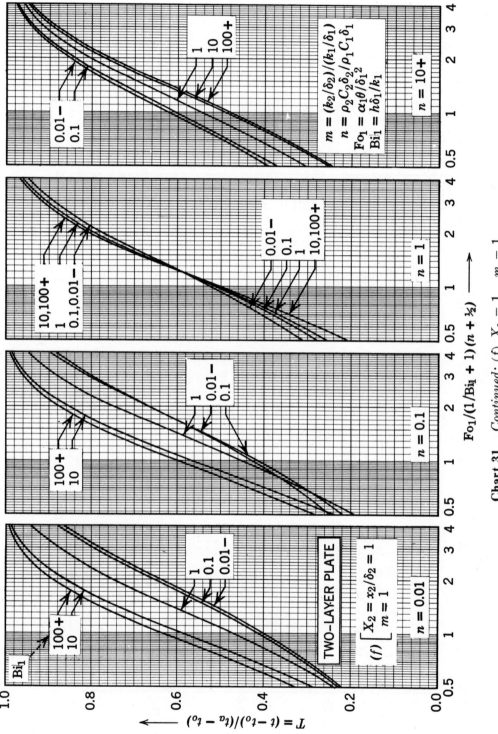

Chart 31. *Continued;* (f) $X_2 = 1$, $m = 1$.

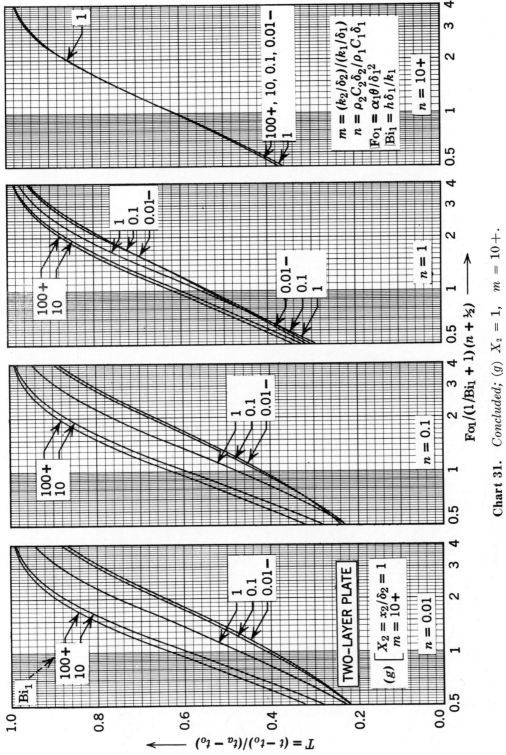

Chart 31. *Concluded;* (g) $X_2 = 1$, $m = 10+$.

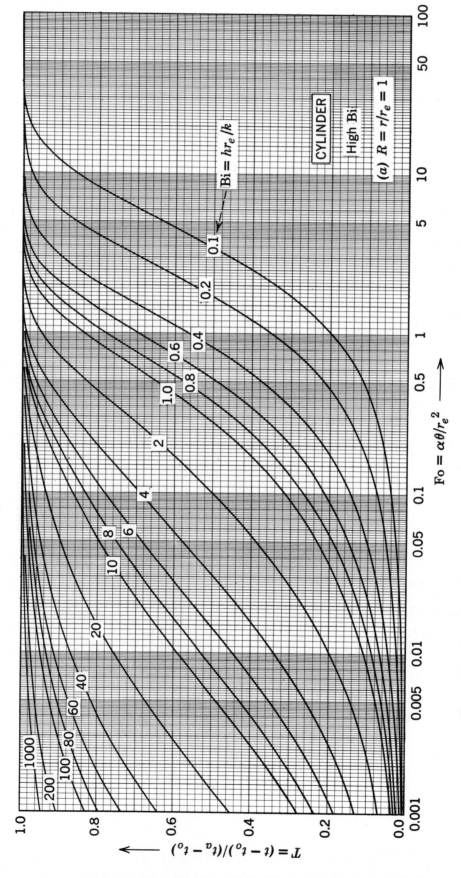

Chart 32. Temperature response of a cylinder, $0 \leq r \leq r_e$, after sudden exposure to a uniform-temperature convective environment t_a at $r = r_e$: high Bi; (a) $R = 1$, (E) *(Continued)*.

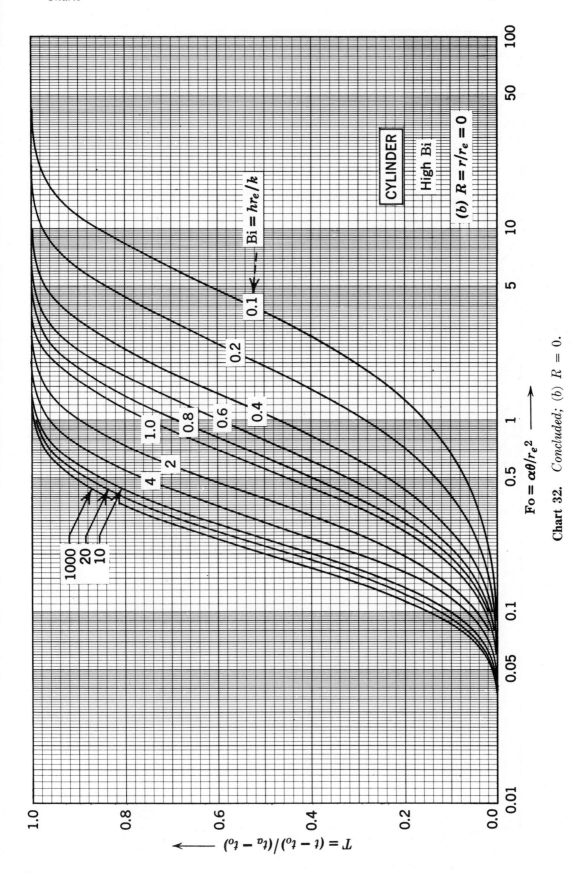

Chart 32. *Concluded;* *(b)* $R = 0$.

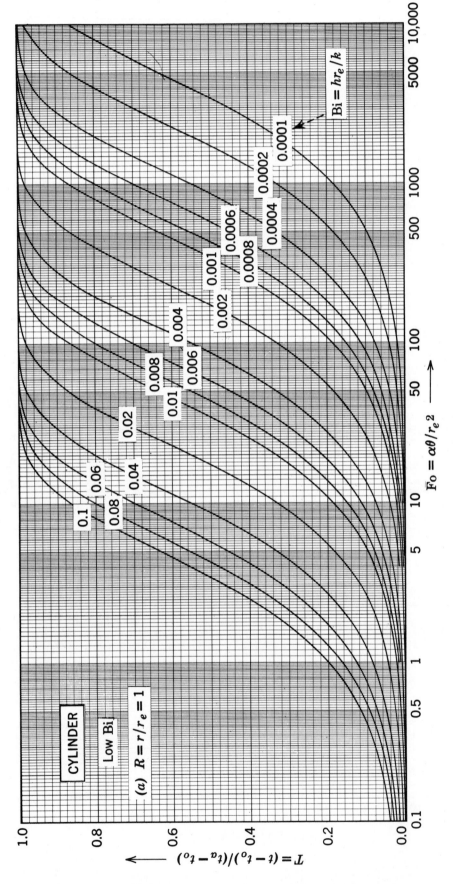

Chart 33. Temperature response of a cylinder, $0 \leq r \leq r_e$, after sudden exposure to a uniform-temperature convective environment t_a at $r = r_e$: low Bi; (a) $R = 1$, (E) (Continued).

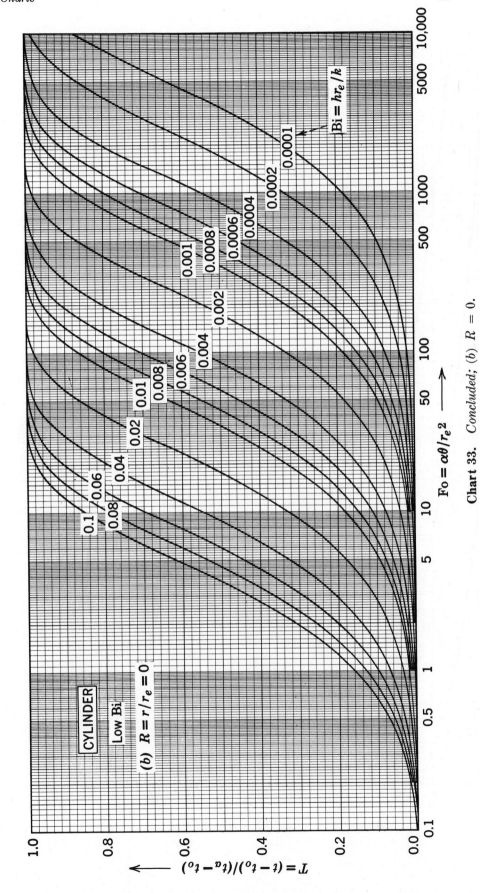

Fo = $\alpha\theta/r_e^2$

CYLINDER

Low Bi

(b) $R = r/r_e = 0$

Bi = hr_e/k

$T = (t - t_0)/(t_a - t_0)$

Chart 33. *Concluded;* (b) $R = 0$.

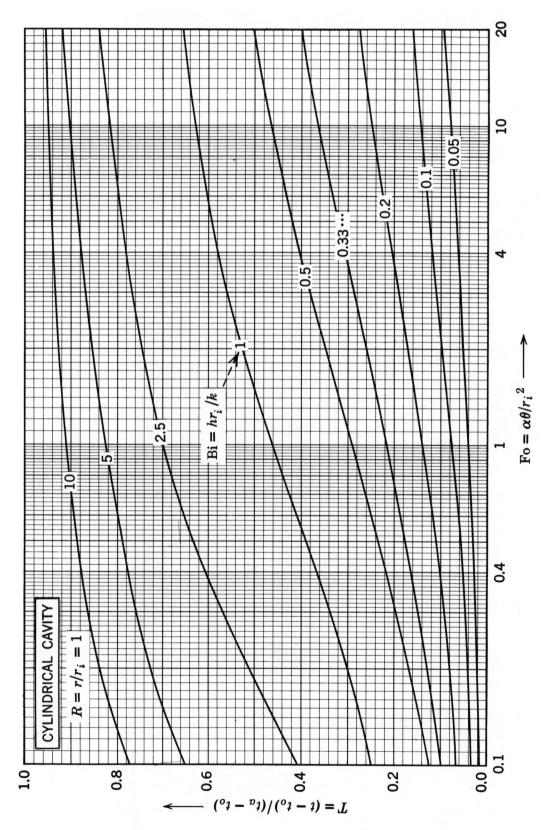

Chart 34. Temperature response of an infinite solid surrounding a cylindrical cavity, $r \geq r_i$, after sudden exposure to a uniform-temperature convective environment t_a at $r = r_i$, (E, E).

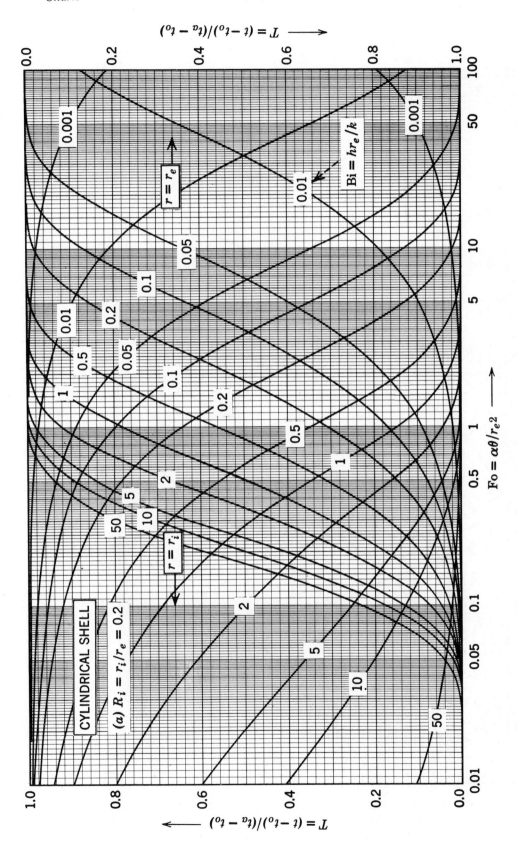

Chart 35. Temperature response of a cylindrical shell, $r_i \leq r \leq r_e$, insulated at its internal surface $r = r_i$ after sudden exposure to a uniform-temperature convective environment t_a at $r = r_e$; (a) $R_i = 0.2$, (E, E) (*Continued*).

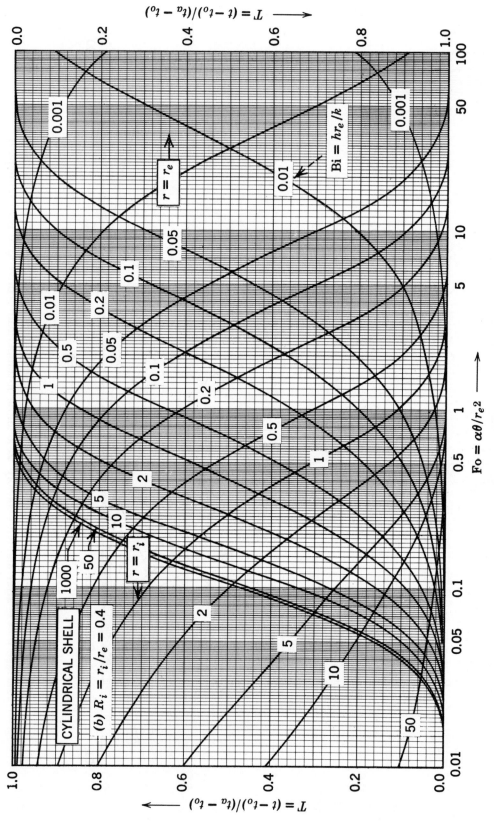

Chart 35. *Continued;* (b) $R_i = 0.4$.

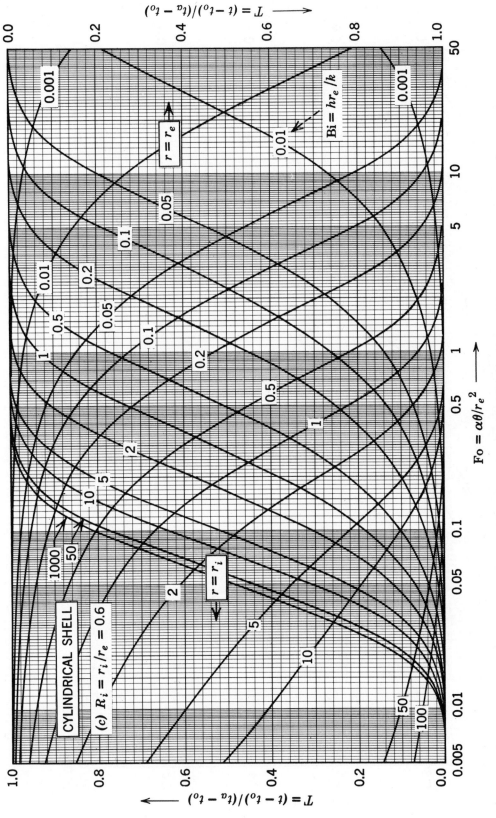

Chart 35. *Continued;* (c) $R_i = 0.6$.

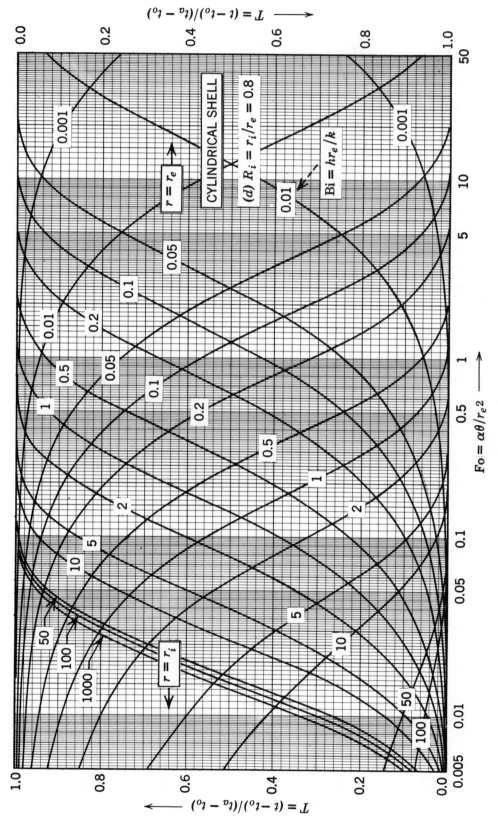

Chart 35. *Continued;* (d) $R_i = 0.8$.

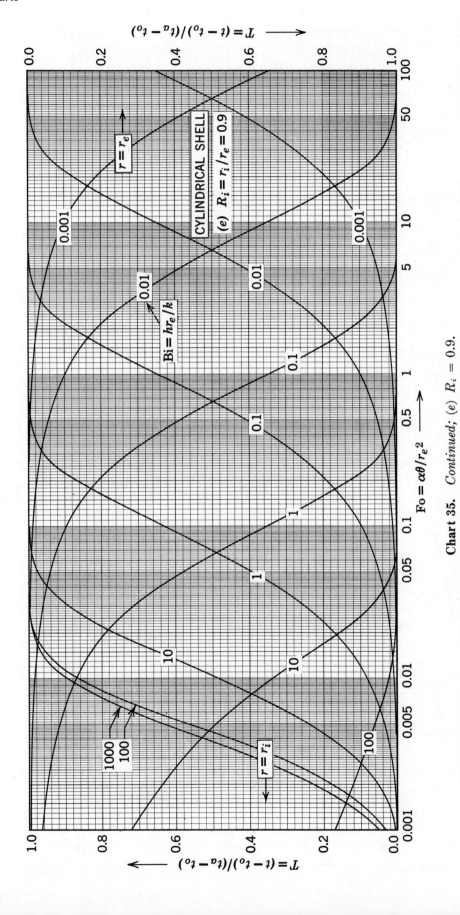

Chart 35. *Continued; (e) $R_i = 0.9$.*

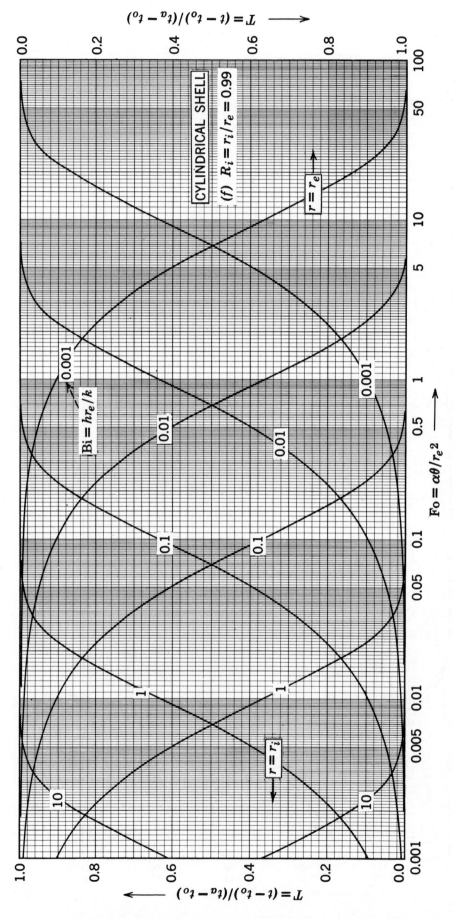

Chart 35. *Concluded;* (f) $R_i = 0.99$.

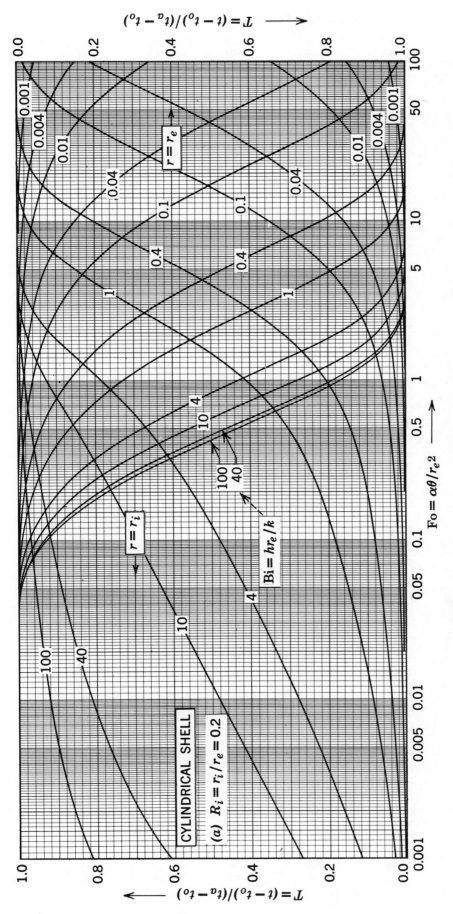

Chart 36. Temperature response of a cylindrical shell, $r_i \leq r \leq r_e$, insulated at its external surface $r = r_e$, after sudden exposure to a uniform-temperature convective environment t_a at $r = r_i$; (a) $R_i = 0.2$, (E, N) (Continued).

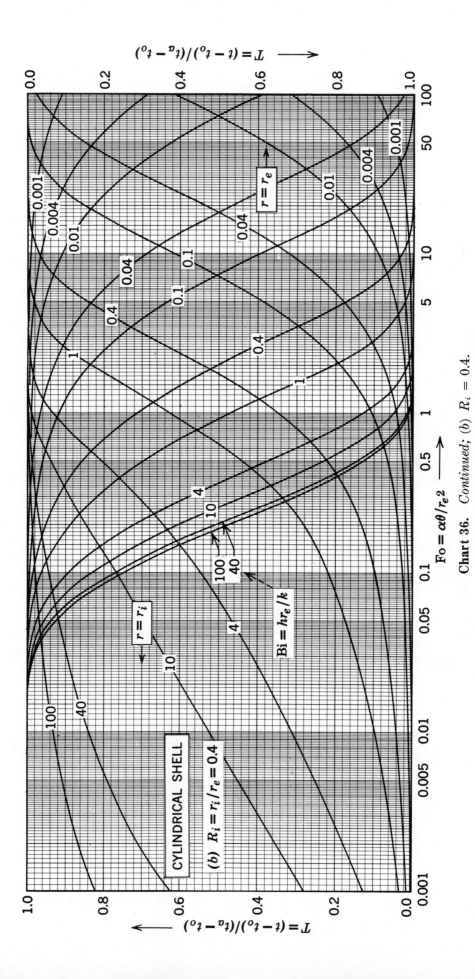

Chart 36. *Continued*; (b) $R_i = 0.4$.

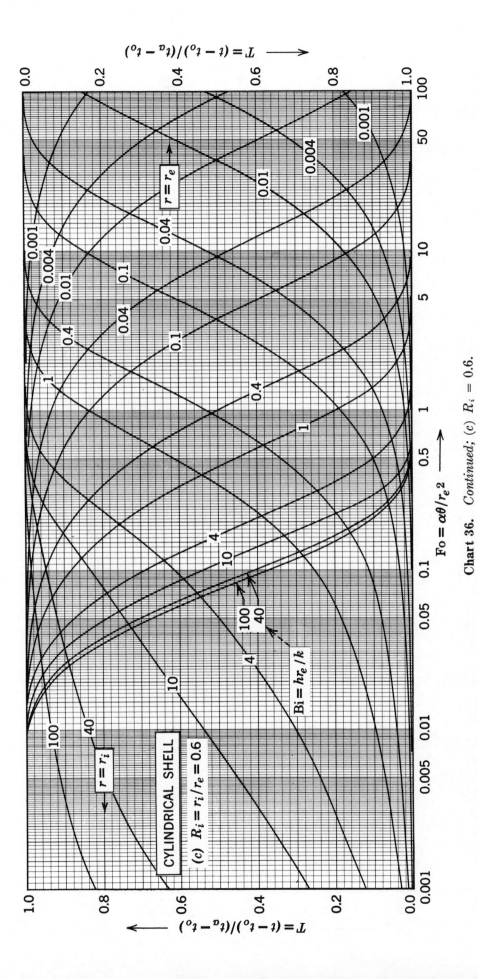

Chart 36. *Continued;* (c) $R_i = 0.6$.

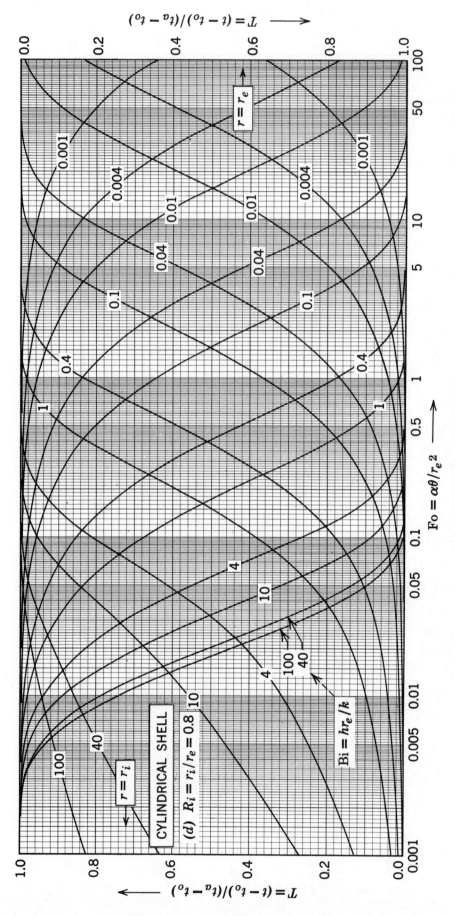

Chart 36. *Continued; (d)* $R_i = 0.8$.

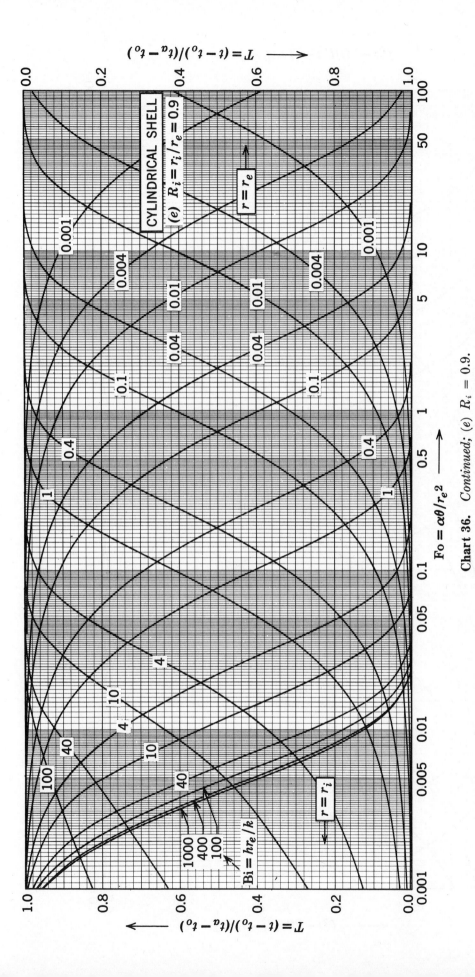

Chart 36. *Continued; (e)* $R_i = 0.9$.

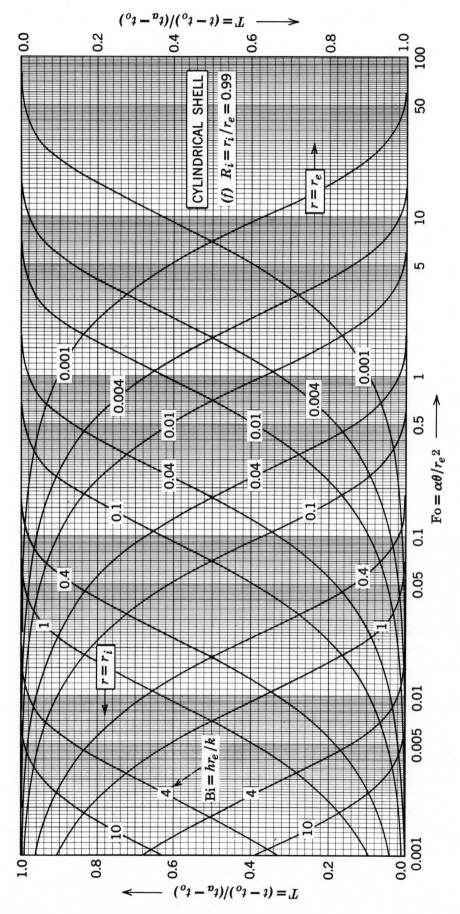

Chart 36. *Concluded; (f)* $R_i = 0.99$.

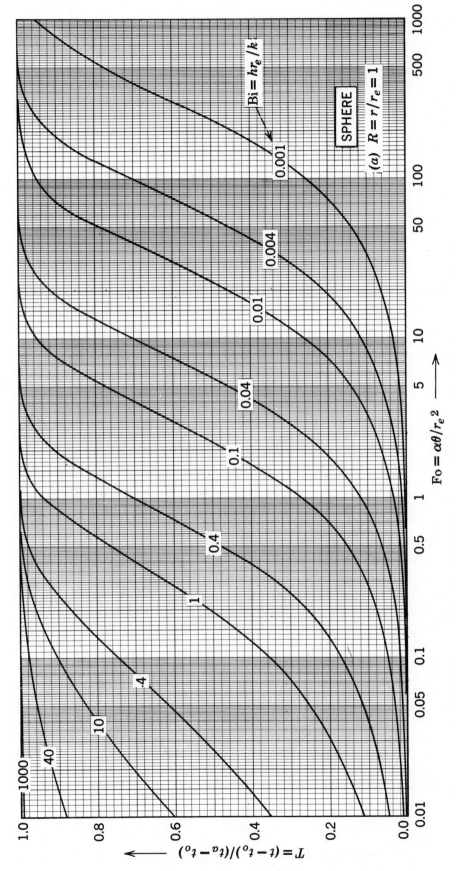

Chart 37. Temperature response of a sphere, $0 \leq r \leq r_e$, after sudden exposure to a uniform-temperature convective environment t_a at $r = r_e$; (a) $R = 1$, (E) (Continued).

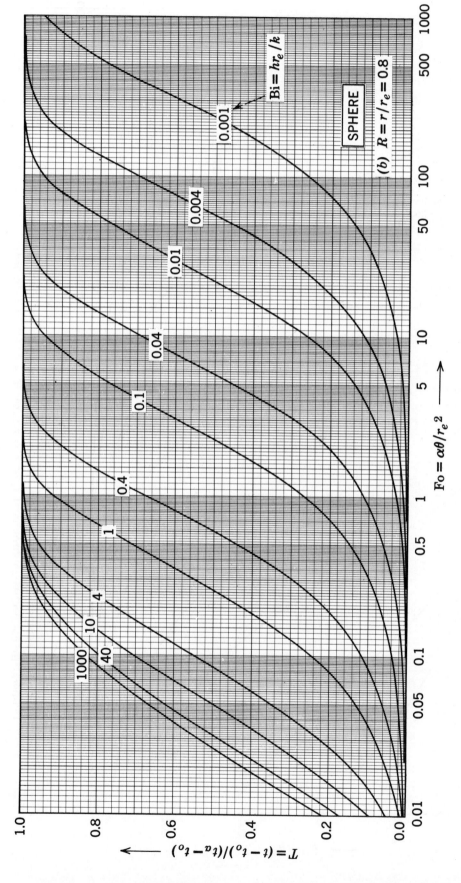

Chart 37. *Continued;* (b) R = 0.8.

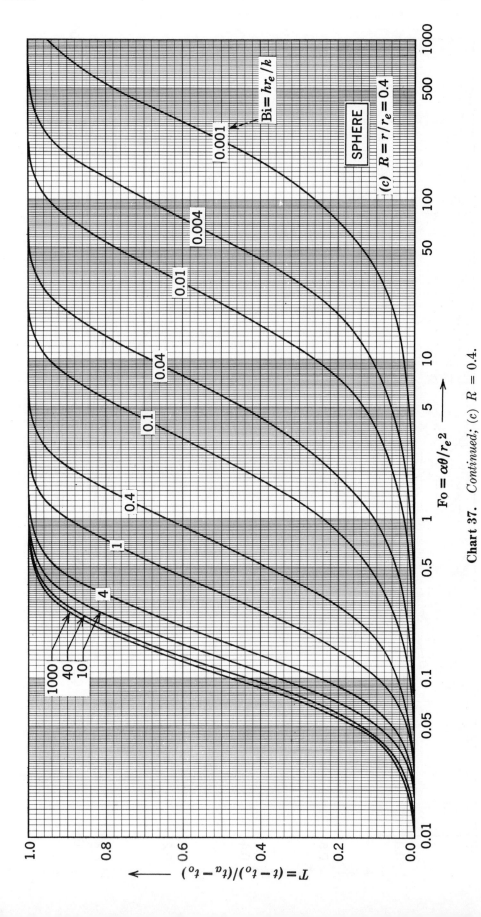

Chart 37. *Continued*; *(c) R* = 0.4.

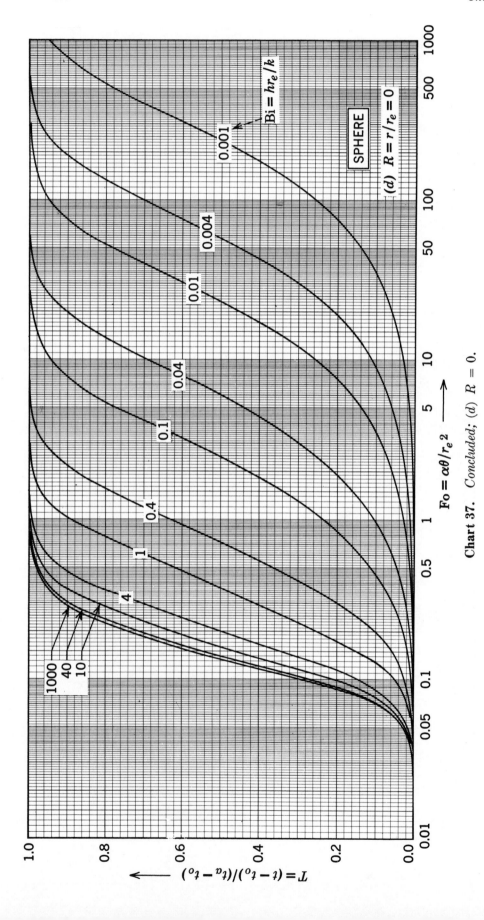

Chart 37. *Concluded;* (*d*) *R* = 0.

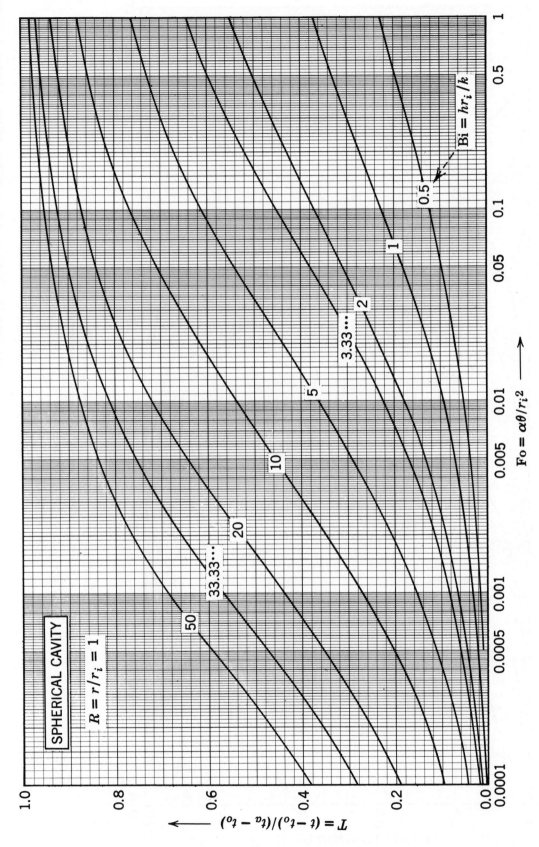

Chart 38. Temperature response of an infinite solid surrounding a spherical cavity, $r \geq r_i$, after sudden exposure to a uniform-temperature convective environment t_a at $r = r_i$, (E).

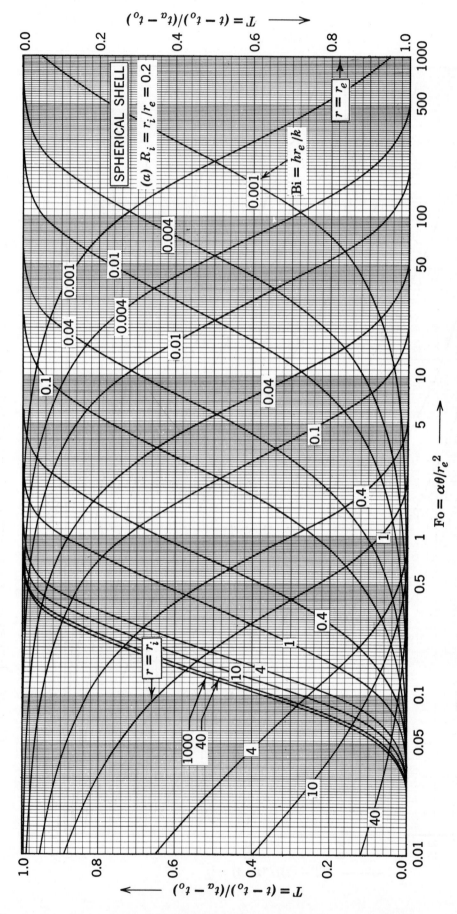

Chart 39. Temperature response of a spherical shell, $r_i \leq r \leq r_e$, insulated at its internal surface $r = r_i$ after sudden exposure to a uniform-temperature convective environment t_a at $r = r_e$; (a) $R_i = 0.2$, (E) (Continued).

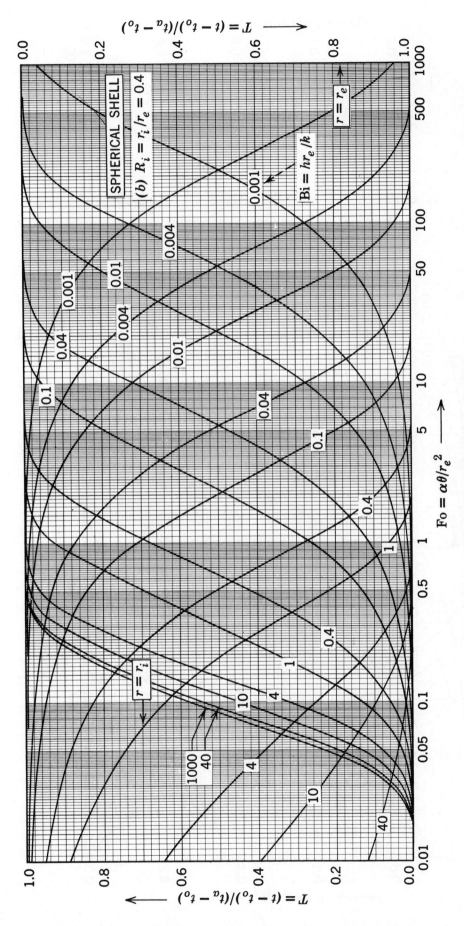

Chart 39. *Continued*; (b) $R_i = 0.4$.

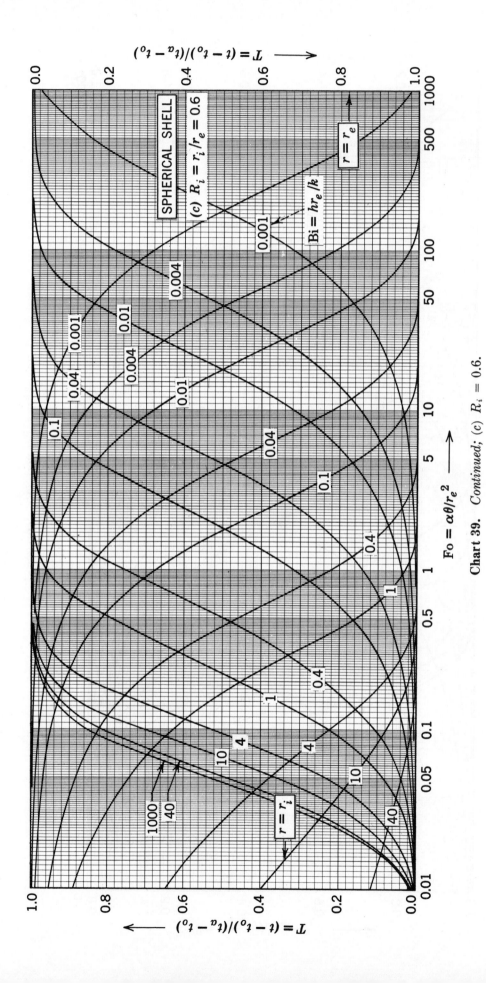

$T = (t - t_0)/(t_a - t_0)$ ⟶

SPHERICAL SHELL

(c) $R_i = r_i/r_e = 0.6$

$r = r_e$

$Bi = hr_e/k$

0.001

0.004

0.01

0.04

0.1

0.001

0.004

0.01

0.04

0.1

0.4

1

$Fo = \alpha\theta/r_e^2$ ⟶

0.4

1

4

10

40

1000

$r = r_i$

4

10

40

⟵ $T = (t - t_0)/(t_a - t_0)$

Chart 39. *Continued;* (c) $R_i = 0.6$.

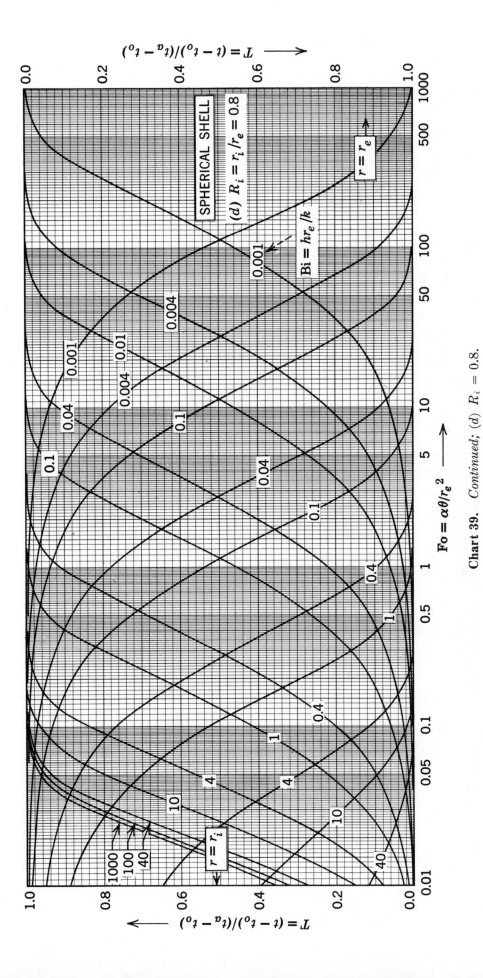

$T = (t - t_o)/(t_a - t_o) \longrightarrow$

SPHERICAL SHELL

(d) $R_i = r_i/r_e = 0.8$

$r = r_e$

Bi $= hr_e/k$

0.001

0.004

0.001

0.004 0.01

0.04

0.1

0.1

0.04

0.1

0.4

1

0.4

1

4

4

10

10

1000

100

40

$r = r_i$

40

Fo $= \alpha\theta/r_e^2 \longrightarrow$

Chart 39. *Continued;* (d) $R_i = 0.8$.

$T = (t - t_o)/(t_a - t_o) \longleftarrow$

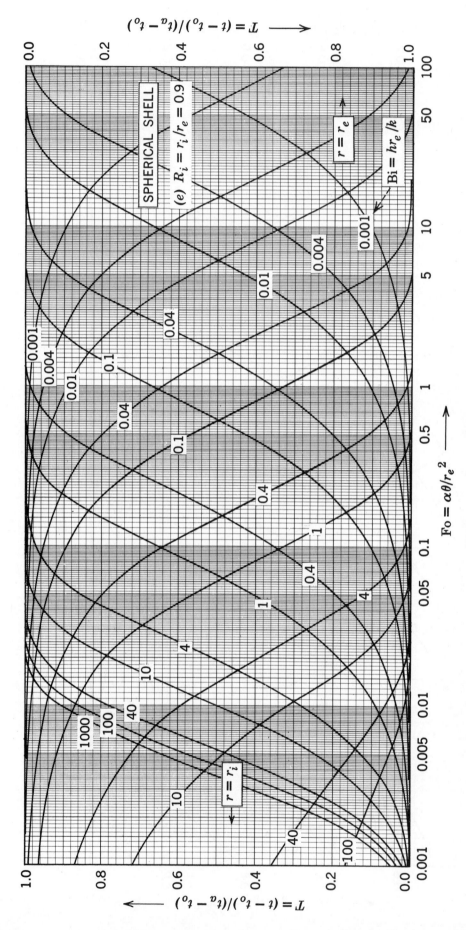

Chart 39. *Continued; (e)* $R_i = 0.9$.

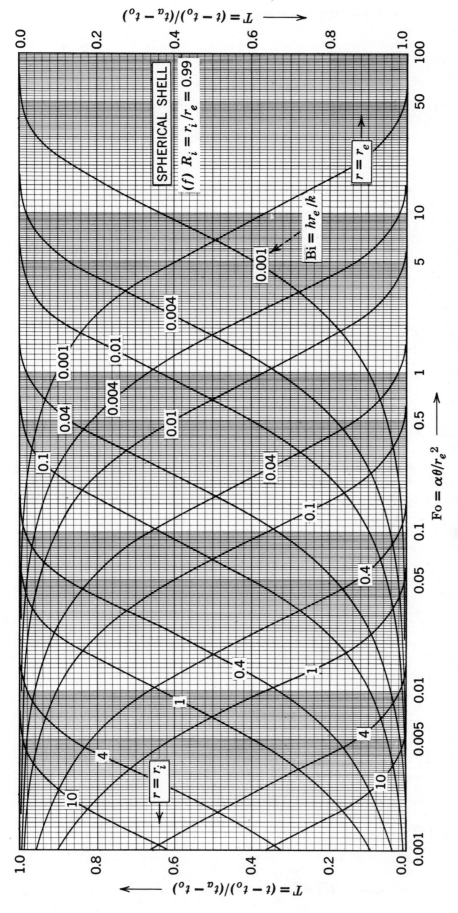

Chart 39. *Concluded;* (f) $R_i = 0.99$.

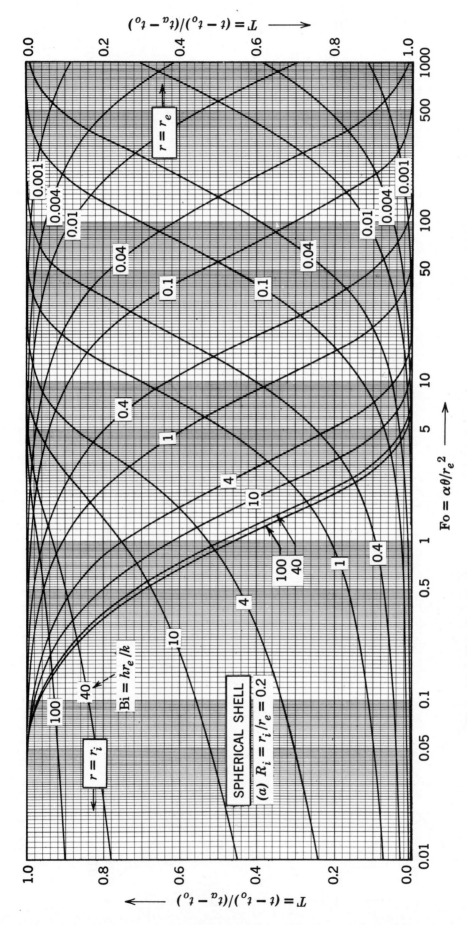

Chart 40. Temperature response of a spherical shell, $r_i \leq r \leq r_e$, insulated at its external surface $r = r_e$ after sudden exposure to a uniform-temperature convective environment t_a at $r = r_i$; (a) $R_i = 0.2$, (E) (*Continued*).

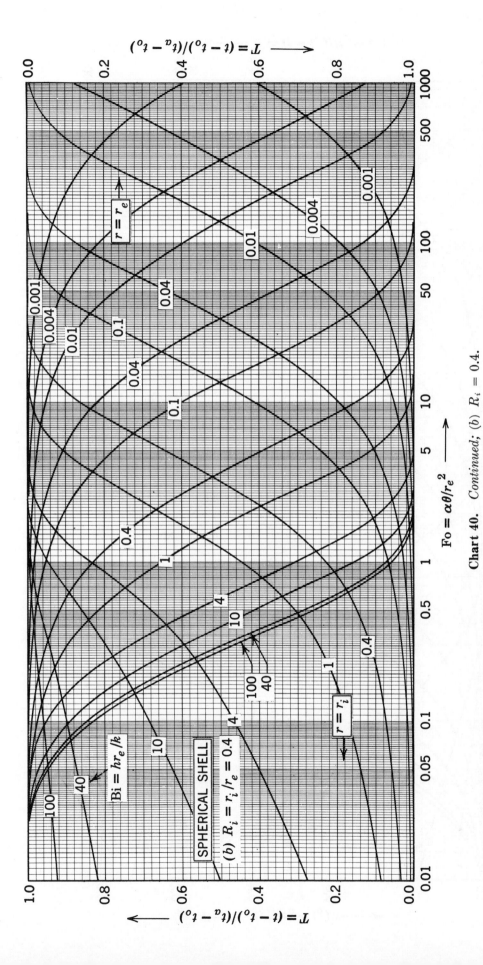

$T = (t - t_o)/(t_a - t_o)$ →

$T = (t - t_o)/(t_a - t_o)$ ←

$Fo = \alpha\theta/r_e^2$ →

$r = r_e$

0.001

0.004

0.01

0.04

0.1

0.4

1

4

10

100

40

$r = r_i$

$Bi = hr_e/k$

SPHERICAL SHELL

(b) $R_i = r_i/r_e = 0.4$

Chart 40. *Continued;* (b) $R_i = 0.4$.

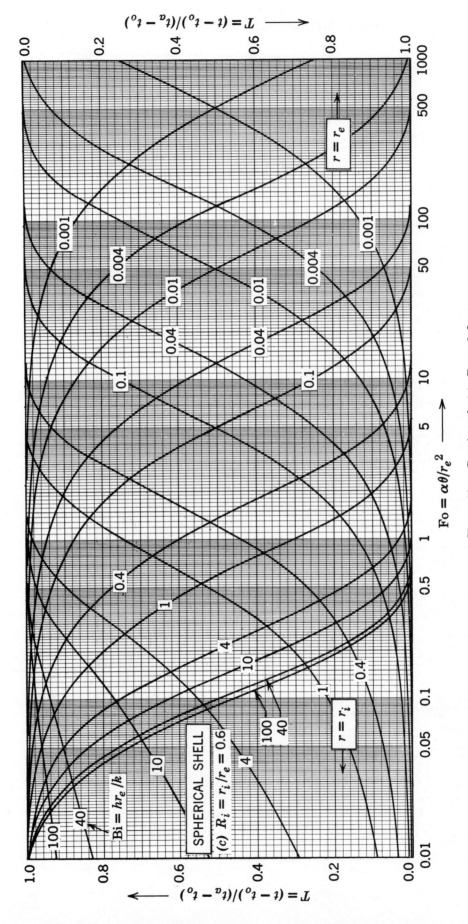

Chart 40. *Continued; (c)* $R_i = 0.6$.

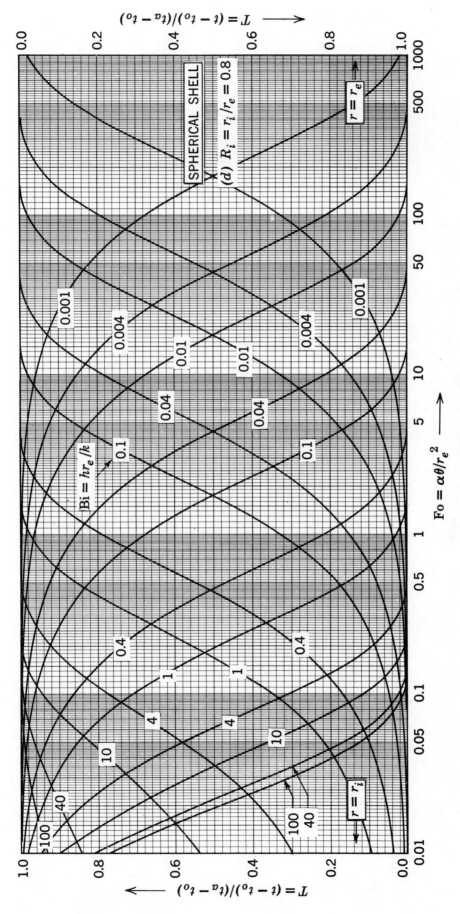

Chart 40. *Continued;* (d) $R_i = 0.8$.

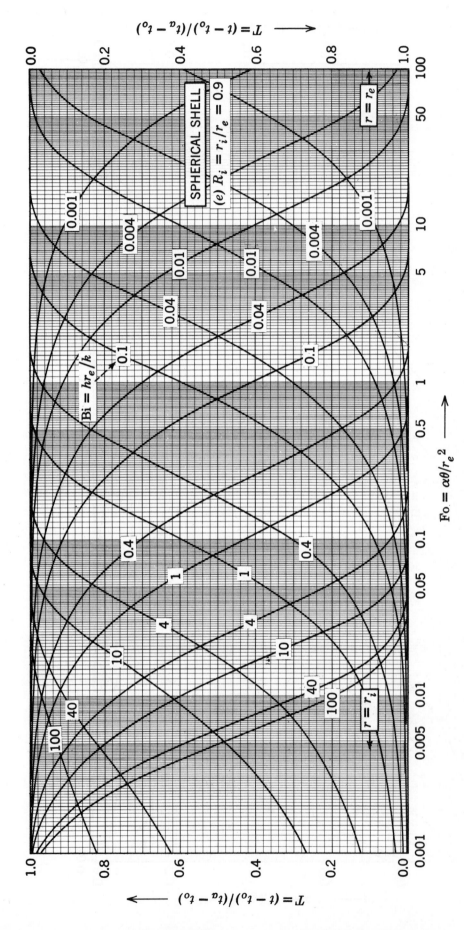

$T = (t - t_0)/(t_a - t_0) \longrightarrow$

$T = (t - t_0)/(t_a - t_0)$

SPHERICAL SHELL

(e) $R_i = r_i/r_e = 0.9$

$Bi = hr_e/k$

$r = r_e$

$r = r_i$

0.001
0.004
0.01
0.04
0.1
0.4
1
4
10
40
100

Fo. $= \alpha\theta/r_e^2 \longrightarrow$

Chart 40. *Continued; (e)* $R_i = 0.9$.

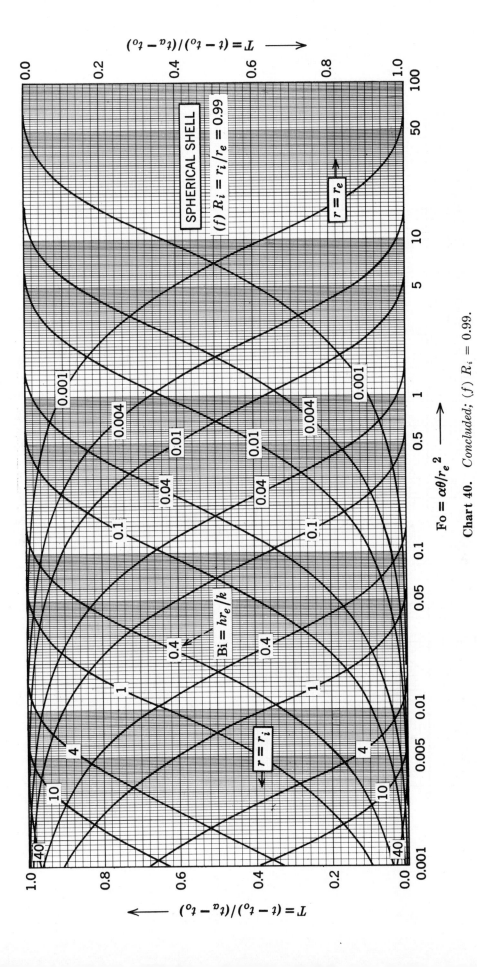

Chart 40. *Concluded;* (f) $R_i = 0.99$.

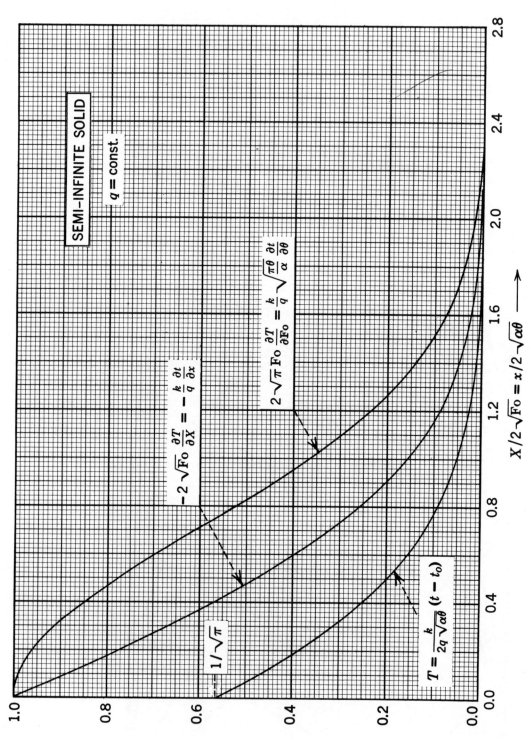

Chart 41. Temperature response, temperature gradient and heating rate in a semi-infinite solid, $x \geq 0$, after sudden exposure to a constant heat input at $x = 0$, (E).

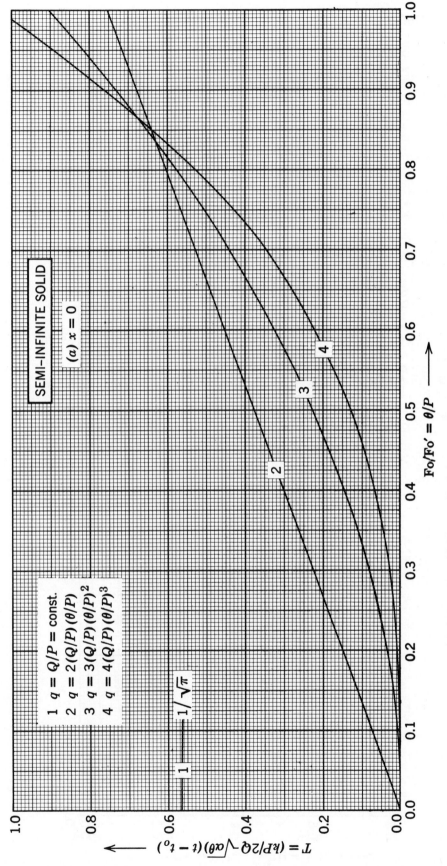

Chart 42. Temperature response of a semi-infinite solid, $x \geq 0$, after sudden exposure to heat inputs at $x = 0$ increasing with the zero, first, second and third power of time; (a) $x = 0$, (E) (*Continued*).

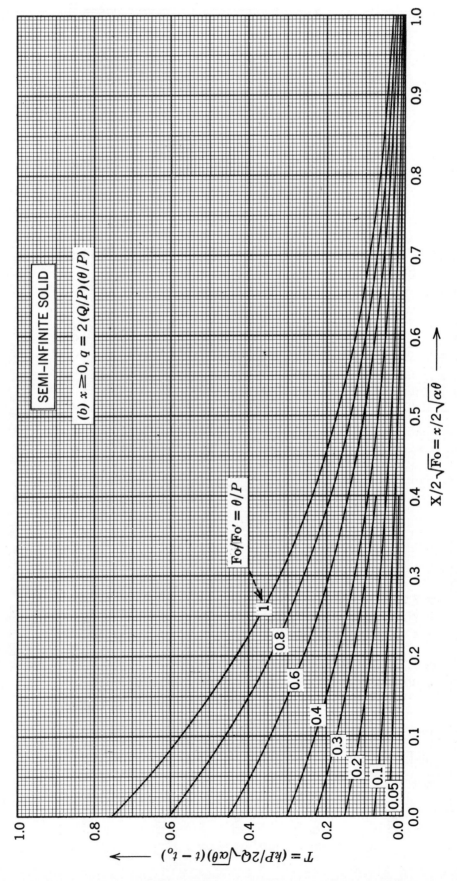

Chart 42. *Continued;* (b) $x \geq 0$, $q = 2(Q/P)(\theta/P)$.

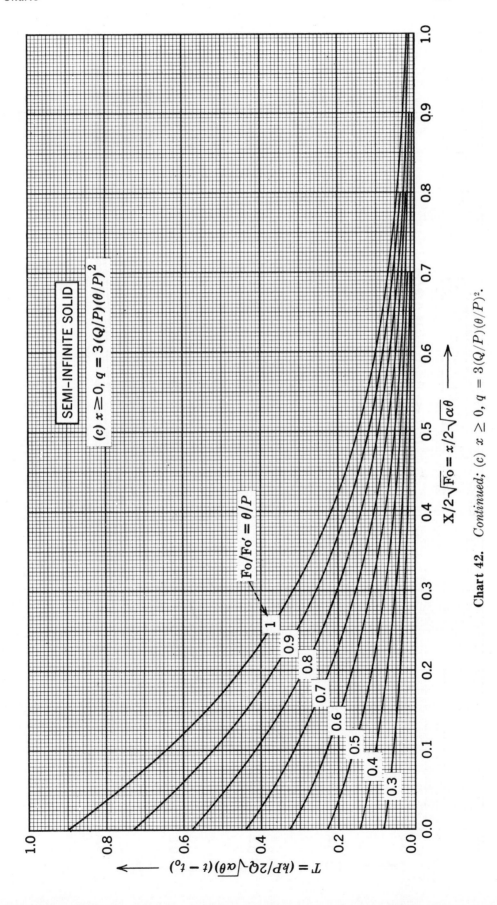

Chart 42. *Continued;* (c) $x \geq 0$, $q = 3(Q/P)(\theta/P)^2$.

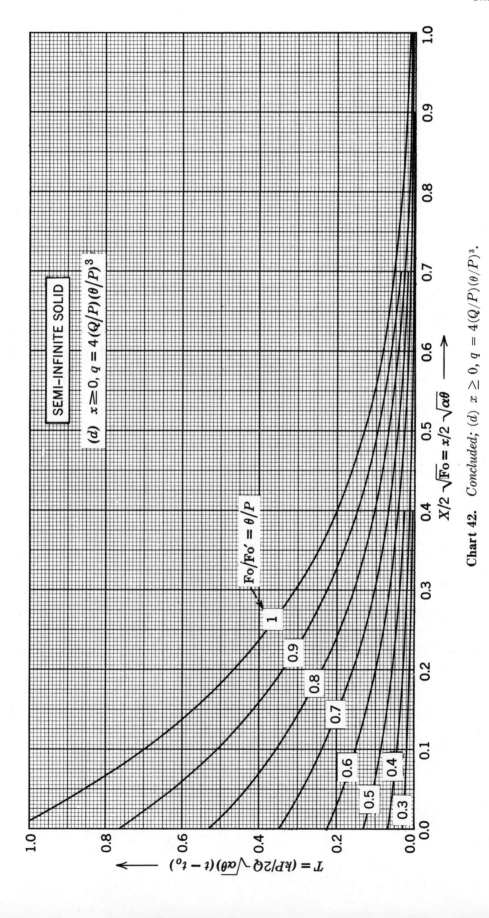

Chart 42. *Concluded*; (d) $x \geq 0$, $q = 4(Q/P)(\theta/P)^3$.

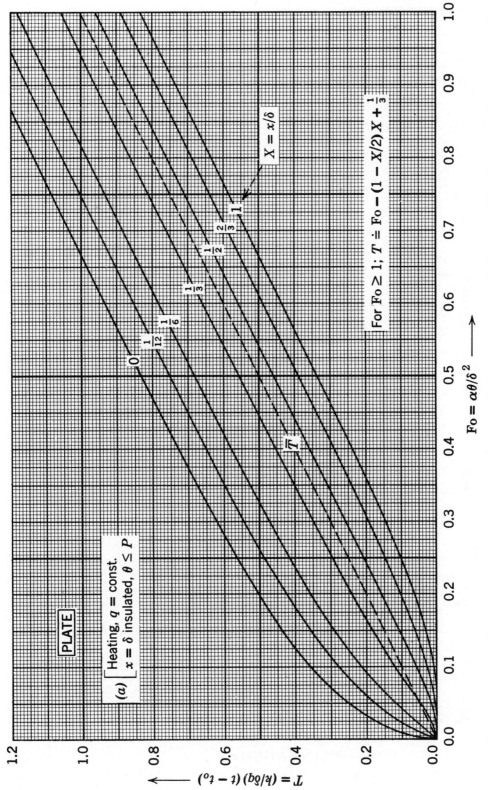

Chart 43. Temperature response of a plate, $0 \leq x \leq \delta$, after sudden exposure to a constant heat input at $x = 0$; (a) Heating, $x = \delta$ insulated, $\theta \leq P$, (E, E) (*Continued*).

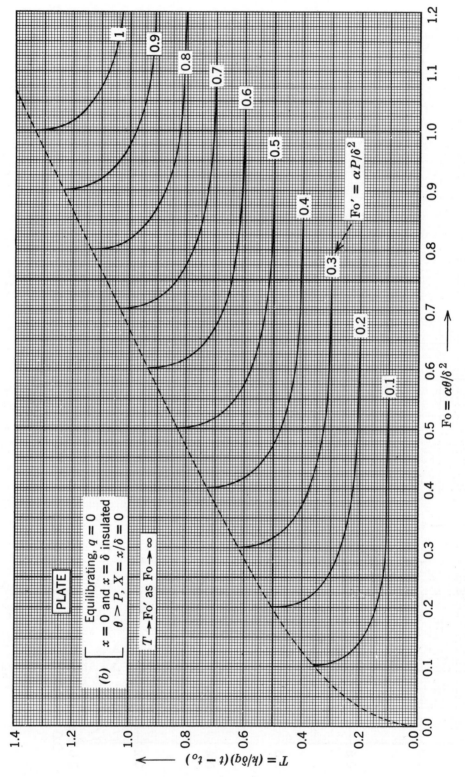

Chart 43. *Continued; (b)* Equilibrating, $q = 0$, $x = 0$ and $x = \delta$ insulated, $\theta > P$, $X = 0$.

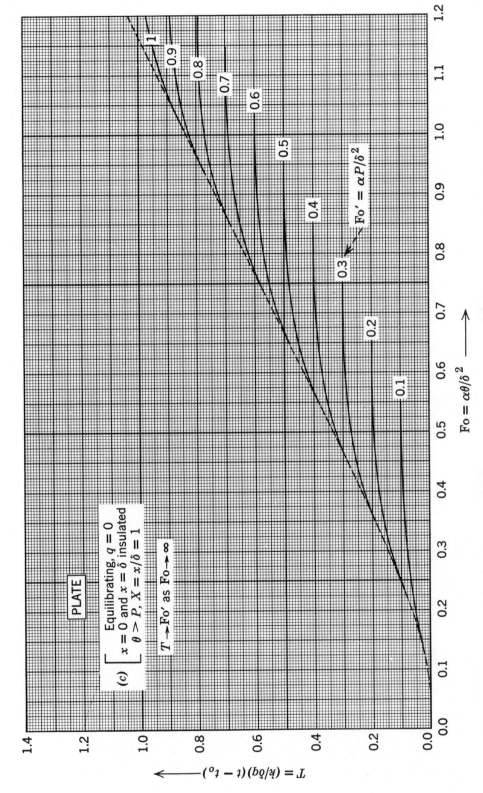

Chart 43. *Concluded;* (c) Equilibrating, $q = 0$, $x = 0$ and $x = \delta$ insulated, $\theta > P$, $X = 1$.

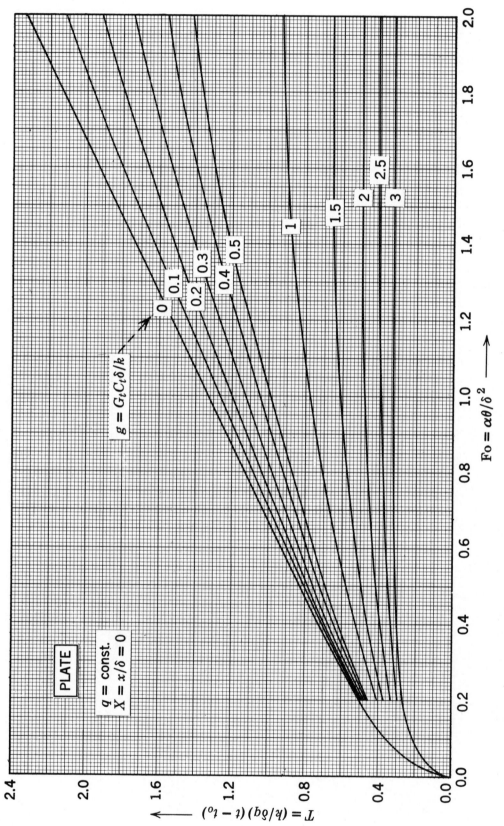

Chart 44. Temperature response of the front surface of a porous plate, $0 \leq x \leq \delta$, after sudden exposure to a constant heat input at $x = 0$ and cooled by a steady flow of transpiration fluid through the plate entering at $x = \delta$ with $t_t = t_0$ at $x \gg \delta$, (E).

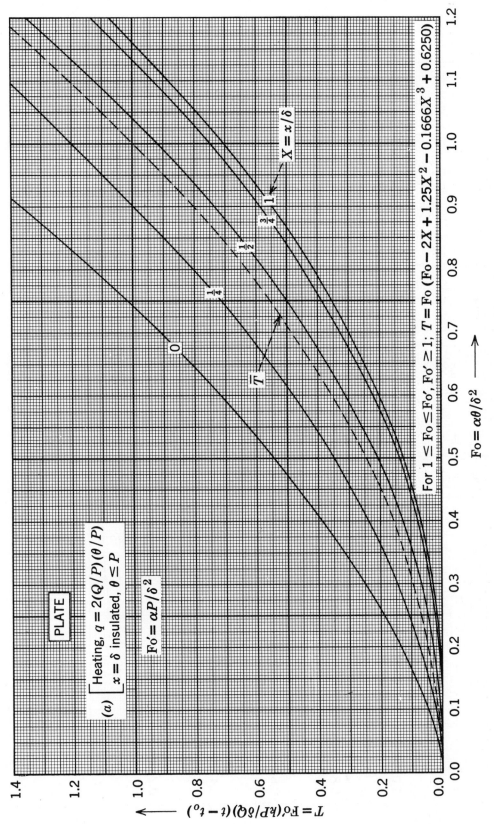

Chart 45. Temperature response of a plate, $0 \leq x \leq \delta$, after sudden exposure to a heat input increasing linearly with time; (*a*) Heating, $x = \delta$ insulated, $\theta \leq P$, (*E, E*) (*Continued*).

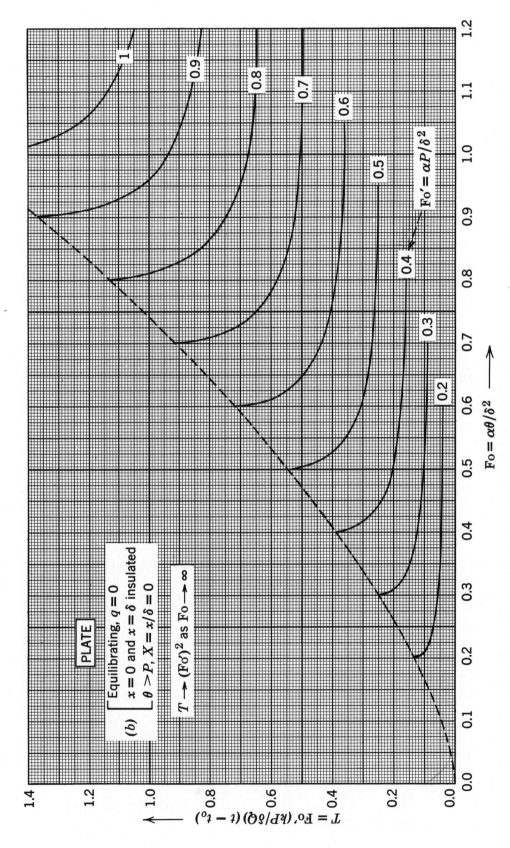

Chart 45. *Continued;* (*b*) Equilibrating, $q = 0$, $x = 0$ and $x = \delta$ insulated, $\theta > P$, $X = 0$.

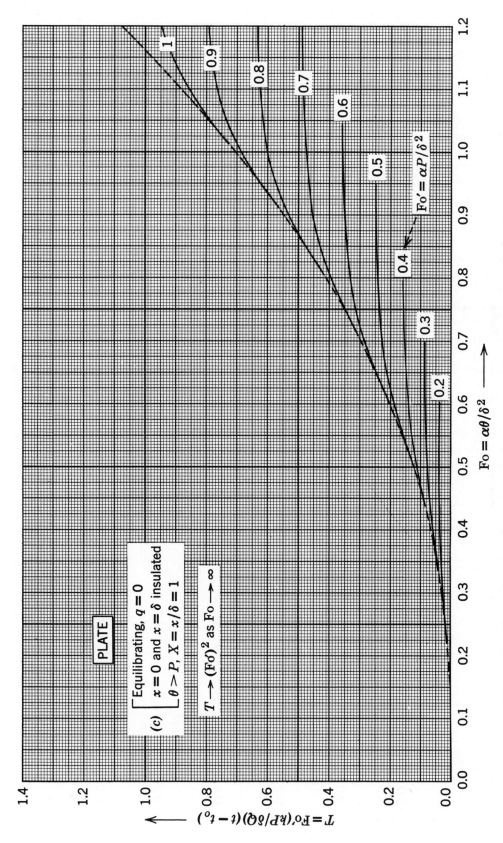

Chart 45. *Concluded;* (c) Equilibrating, $q = 0$, $x = 0$ and $x = \delta$ insulated, $\theta > P$, $X = 1$.

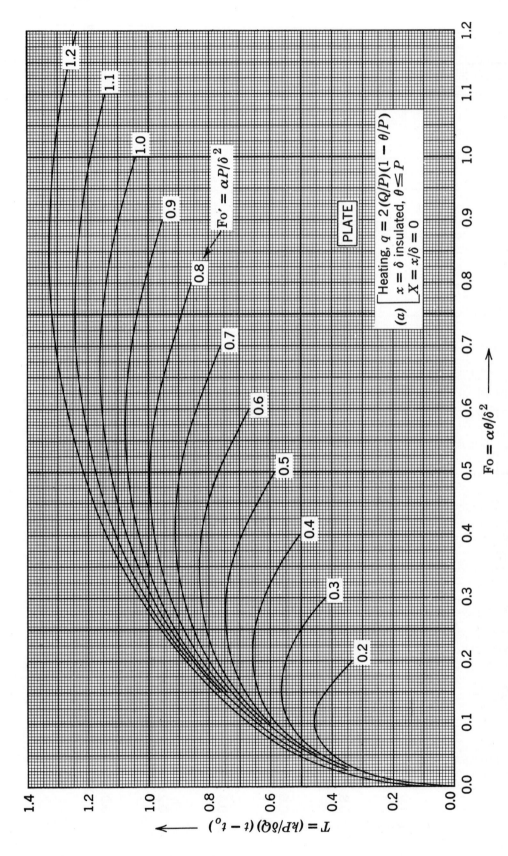

$Fo = \alpha\theta/\delta^2 \longrightarrow$

$T = (k P/\delta Q)(t - t_o) \longleftarrow$

$Fo' = \alpha P/\delta^2$

PLATE

$(a) \begin{bmatrix} \text{Heating, } q = 2(Q/P)(1 - \theta/P) \\ x = \delta \text{ insulated, } \theta \le P \\ X = x/\delta = 0 \end{bmatrix}$

Chart 46. Temperature response of a plate, $0 \le x \le \delta$, after sudden exposure to a heat input decreasing linearly with time; (a) Heating, $x = \delta$ insulated, $\theta \le P$, $X = 0$, (E) (Continued).

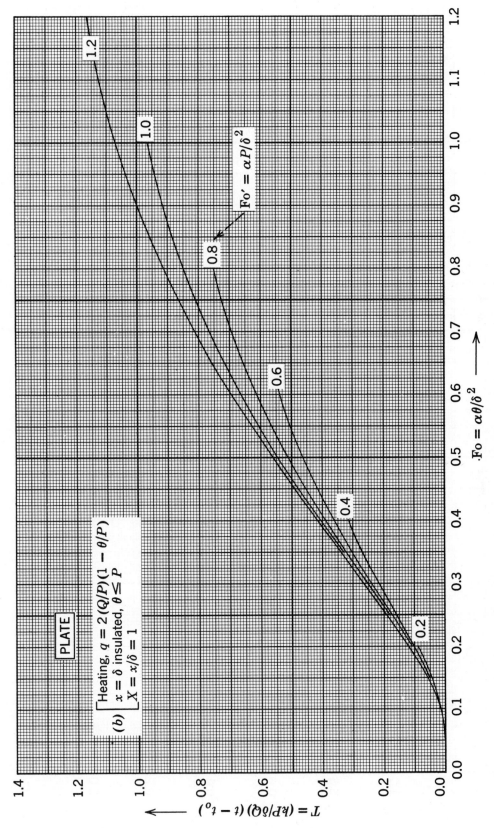

Chart 46. *Continued;* (*b*) Heating, $x = \delta$ insulated, $\theta \le P$, $X = 1$.

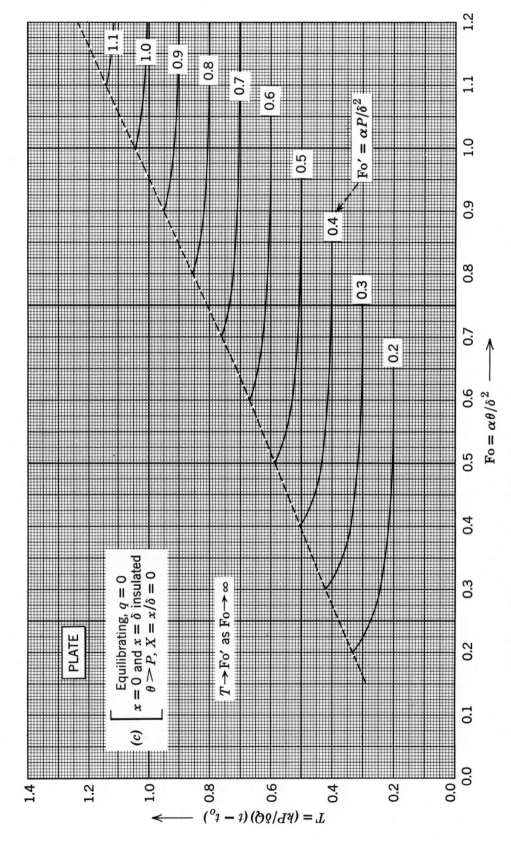

PLATE

(c) $\left[\begin{array}{l} \text{Equilibrating, } q = 0 \\ x = 0 \text{ and } x = \delta \text{ insulated} \\ \theta > P, \; X = x/\delta = 0 \end{array}\right.$

$T \rightarrow \text{Fo}'$ as $\text{Fo} \rightarrow \infty$

$\text{Fo}' = \alpha P/\delta^2$

0.2
0.3
0.4
0.5
0.6
0.7
0.8
0.9
1.0
1.1

$\text{Fo} = \alpha\theta/\delta^2 \longrightarrow$

$T = (k P/\delta Q)(t - t_o) \longleftarrow$

Chart 46. *Continued;* (c) Equilibrating, $q = 0$, $x = 0$ and $x = \delta$ insulated, $\theta > P$, $X = 0$.

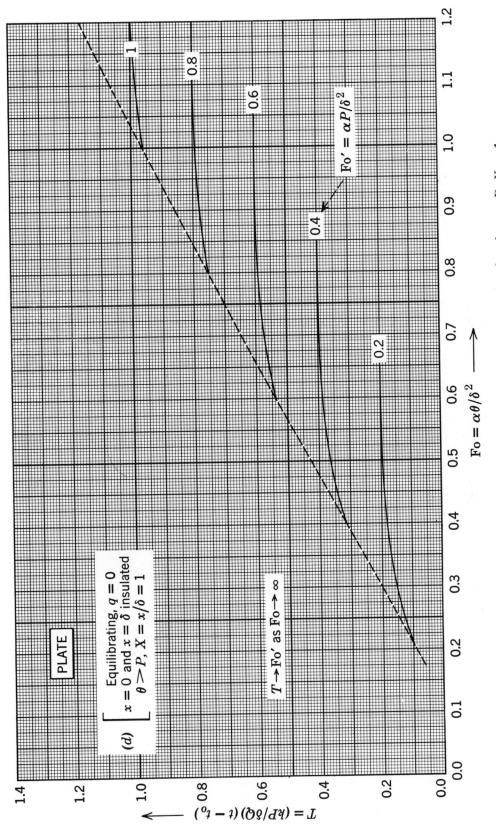

Chart 46. *Concluded;* (d) Equilibrating, $q = 0$, $x = 0$ and $x = \delta$ insulated, $\theta > P$, $X = 1$.

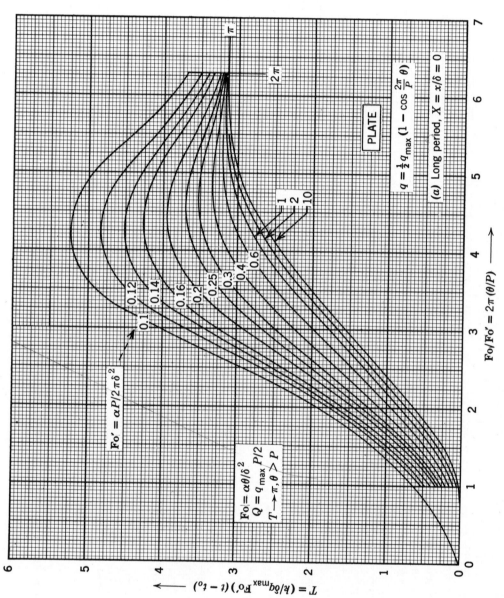

Chart 47. Temperature response of a plate, $0 \leq x \leq \delta$, with insulated back face $x = \delta$ after sudden exposure to a heat input at $x = 0$ varying as a cosine pulse with time; (*a*) Long period, $X = 0$, (*E*, *E*) (*Continued*).

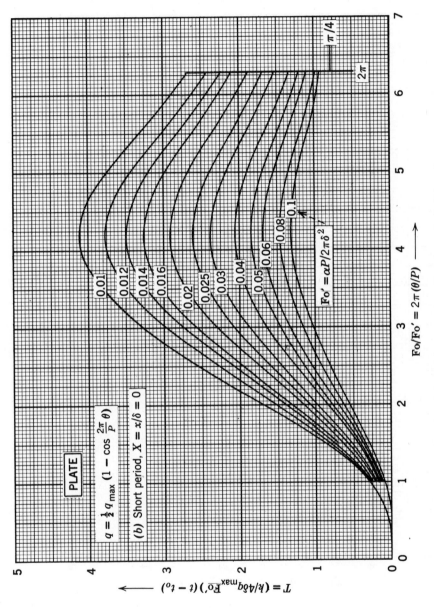

Chart 47. *Continued;* (b) Short period, $X = 0$.

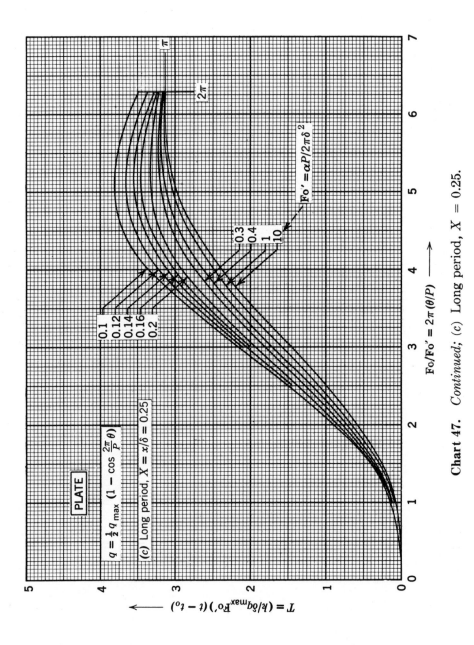

Chart 47. *Continued; (c)* Long period, $X = 0.25$.

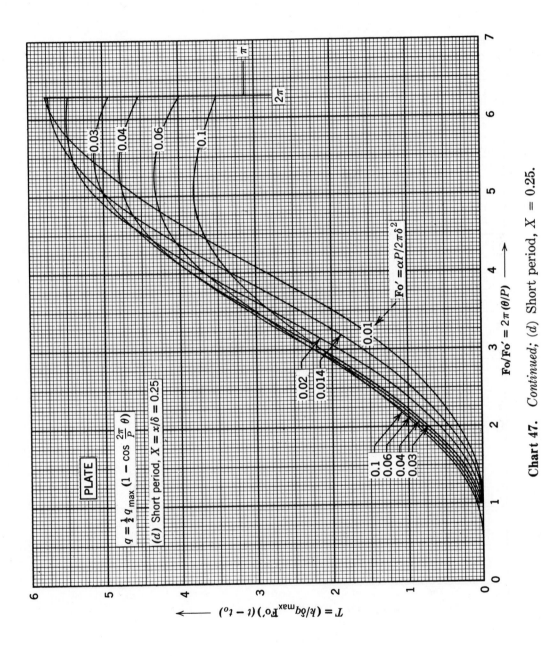

Chart 47. *Continued;* (*d*) Short period, $X = 0.25$.

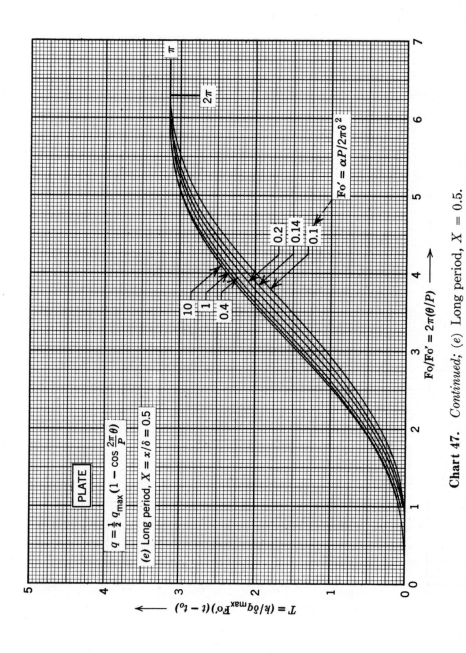

PLATE

$$q = \tfrac{1}{2}\, q_{max}\left(1 - \cos \tfrac{2\pi}{P}\theta\right)$$

(e) Long period, $X = x/\delta = 0.5$

$Fo/Fo' = 2\pi(\theta/P) \longrightarrow$

$Fo' = \alpha P/2\pi\delta^2$

$T = (k/\delta q_{max} Fo')(t - t_0) \longleftarrow$

Chart 47. *Continued;* (e) Long period, $X = 0.5$.

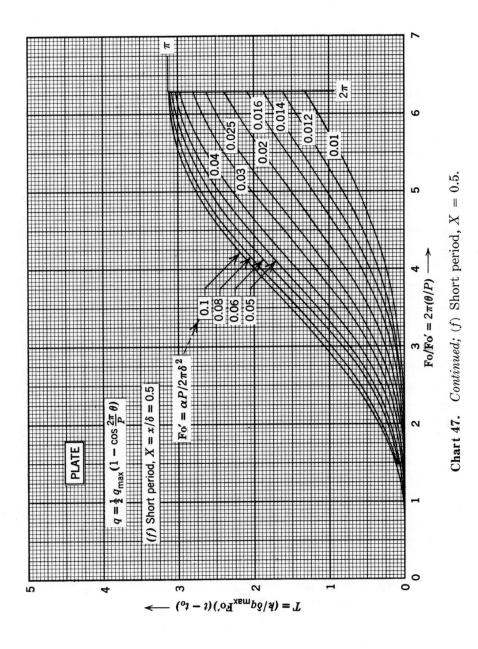

Chart 47. *Continued;* (f) Short period, $X = 0.5$.

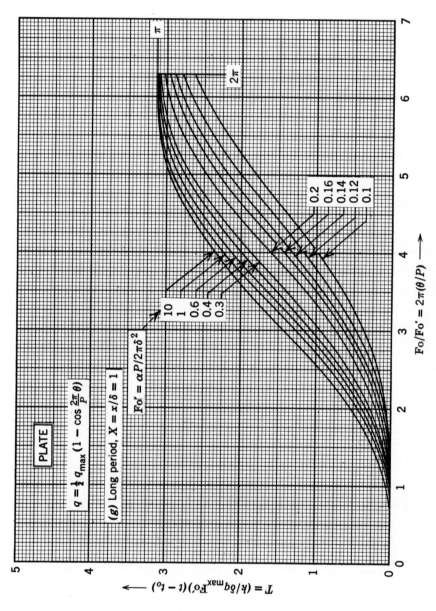

Chart 47. *Continued;* *(g)* Long period, $X = 1$.

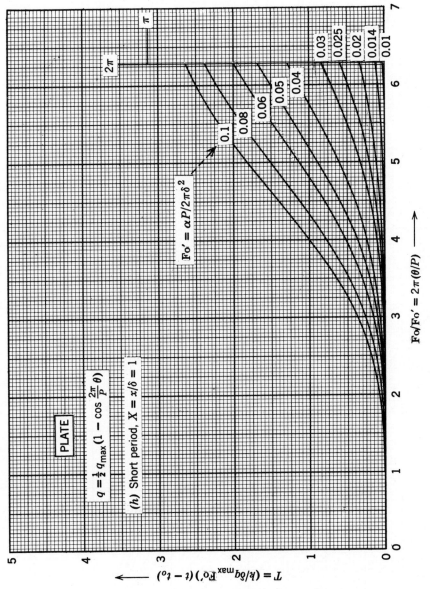

Chart 47. *Concluded;* (h) Short period, X = 1.

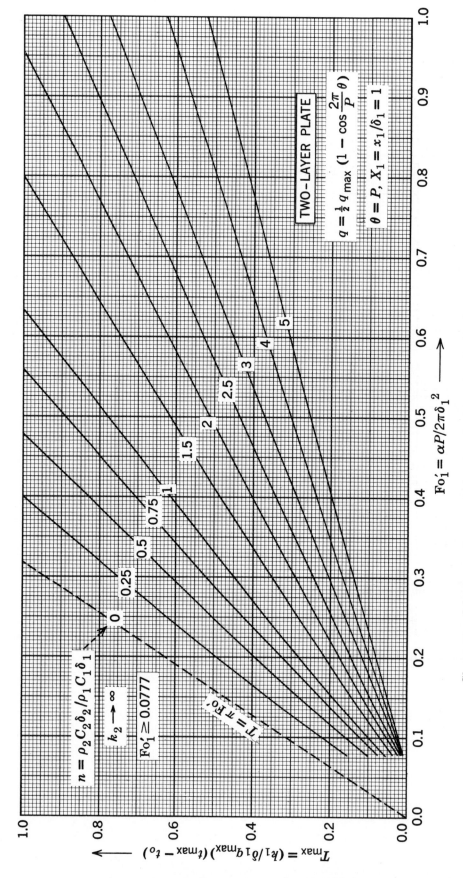

Chart 48. Maximum temperature at end of heating ($\theta = P$) of the back layer of a two-layer plate, $0 \le x_1 \le \delta_1$ and $0 \le x_2 \le \delta_2$, with back layer insulated at $x_2 = \delta_2$ and of infinite internal conductance after sudden exposure to a heat input at $x_1 = 0$ varying as a cosine pulse with time, (I).

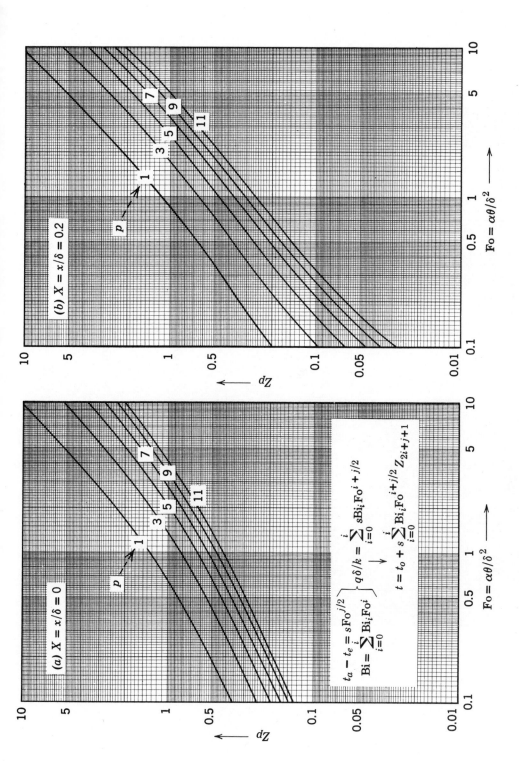

Chart 49. Temperature response function for a plate, $0 \leq x \leq \delta$, with insulated back face $x = \delta$ after sudden exposure to a general heat input at $x = 0$ dependent on time; (a) $X = 0$, (b) $X = 0.2$, (E, E) (*Continued*).

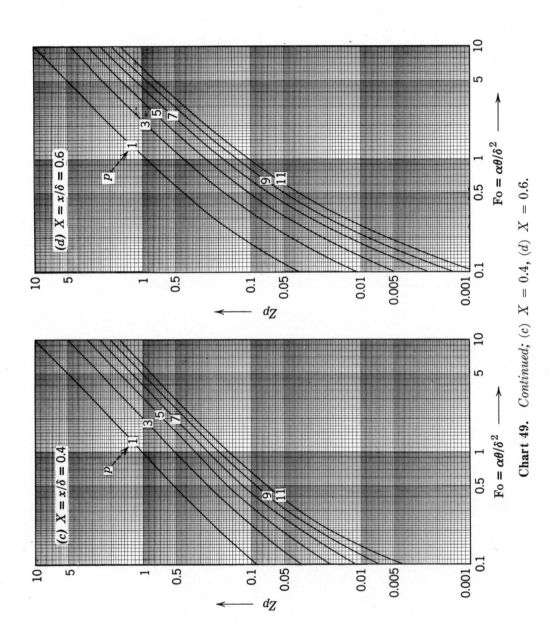

Chart 49. *Continued; (c)* $X = 0.4$, *(d)* $X = 0.6$.

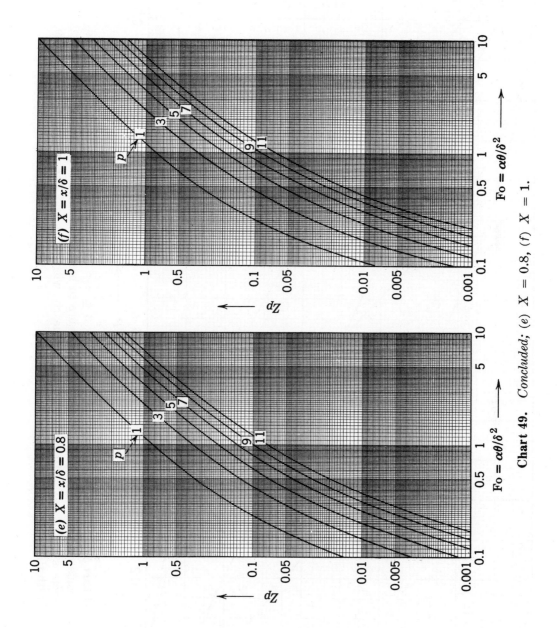

Chart 49. *Concluded;* (e) $X = 0.8$, (f) $X = 1$.

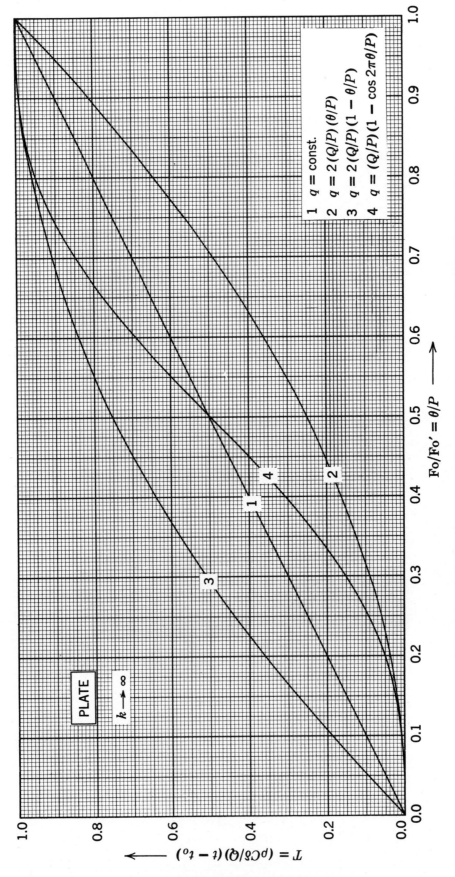

Chart 50. Temperature response of a plate, $0 \leq x \leq \delta$, of infinite internal conductance and insulated back face $x = \delta$ after sudden exposure to heat inputs at $x = 0$ constant with time, increasing linearly with time, decreasing linearly with time, and varying as a cosine pulse with time, (E).

Legend inside chart:

1 $q = $ const.
2 $q = 2\,(Q/P)\,(\theta/P)$
3 $q = 2\,(Q/P)\,(1 - \theta/P)$
4 $q = (Q/P)(1 - \cos 2\pi\theta/P)$

Axis labels:

$Fo/Fo' = \theta/P \longrightarrow$

$T = (\rho C\delta/Q)(t - t_0) \longleftarrow$

PLATE
$k \longrightarrow \infty$

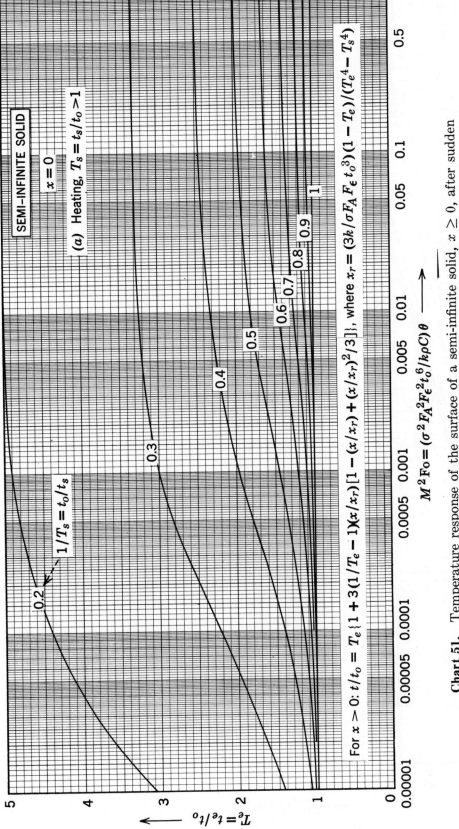

Chart 51. Temperature response of the surface of a semi-infinite solid, $x \geq 0$, after sudden exposure to a constant-temperature radiation heat source or sink t_s at $x = 0$; (*a*) Heating, $T_s > 1$, (*I*) (*Continued*).

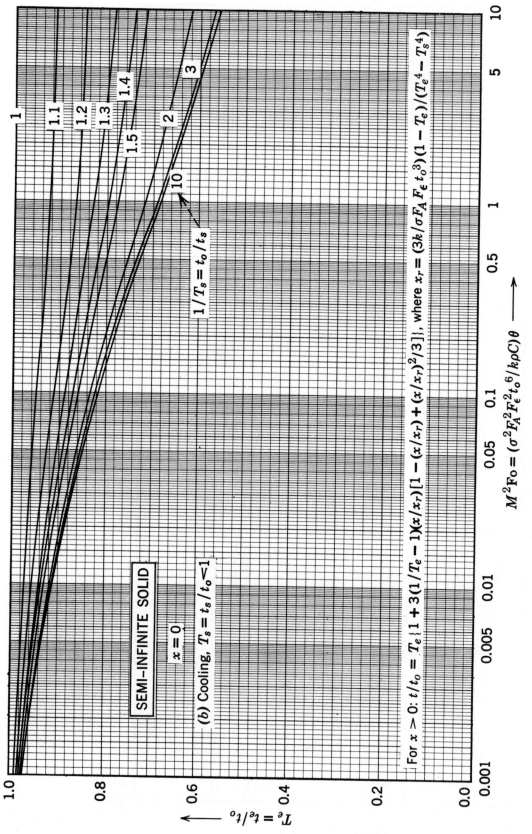

Chart 51. *Concluded;* (b) Cooling, $T_s < 1$.

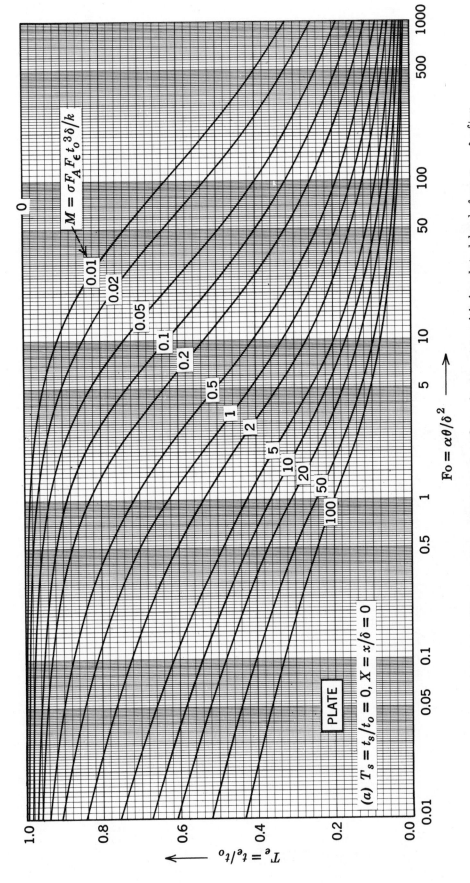

Chart 52. Temperature response of a plate, $0 \leq x \leq \delta$, with insulated back face $x = \delta$ after sudden exposure to a constant-temperature radiation heat sink t_s at $x = 0$; (a) $T_s = 0$, $X = 0$, (I) $(Continued)$.

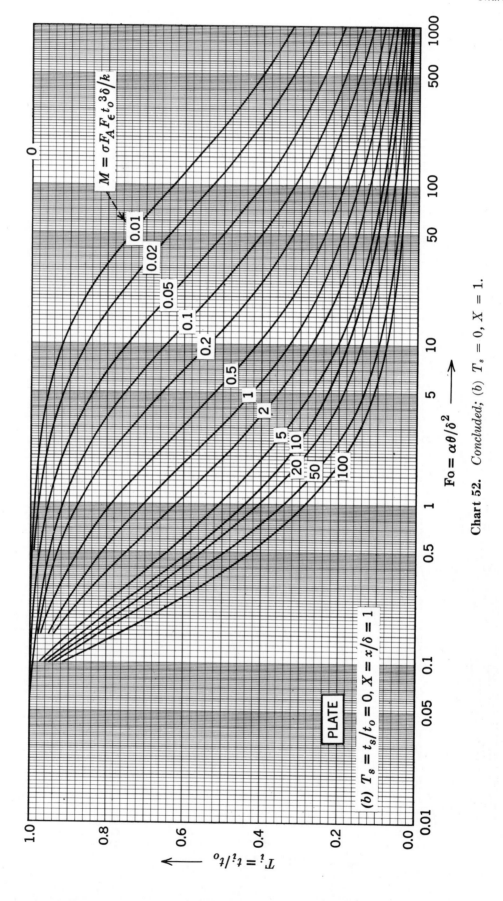

$$\text{Fo} = \alpha\theta/\delta^2 \longrightarrow$$

Chart 52. *Concluded;* (b) $T_s = 0$, $X = 1$.

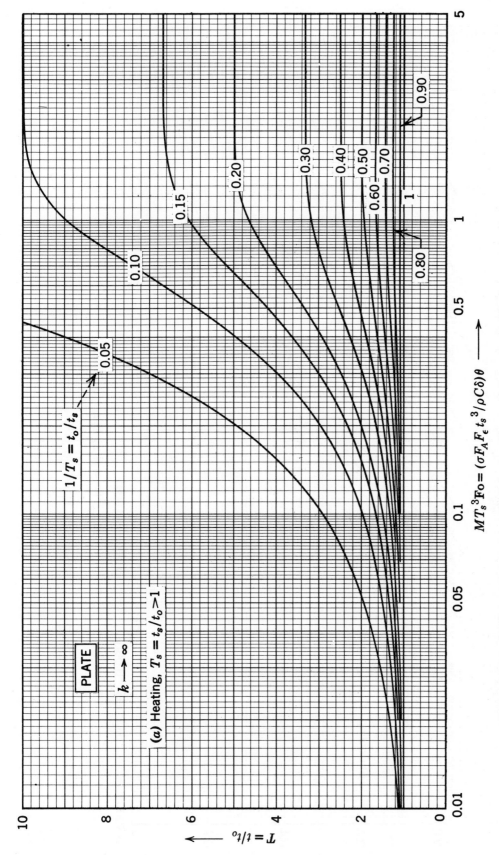

Chart 53. Temperature response of a plate, $0 \leq x \leq \delta$, of infinite internal conductance and with insulated back face $x = \delta$ after sudden exposure to a constant-temperature radiation heat source or sink t_s at $x = 0$; (a) Heating, $T_s > 1$, (E) (*Continued*).

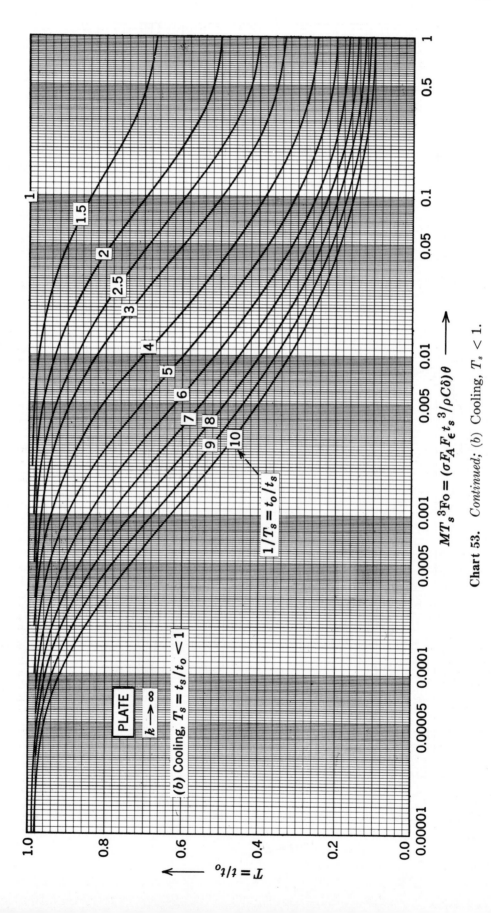

$MT_s{}^3\mathrm{Fo} = (\sigma F_A F_\epsilon t_s{}^3/\rho C\delta)\theta \longrightarrow$

Chart 53. *Continued; (b)* Cooling, $T_s < 1$.

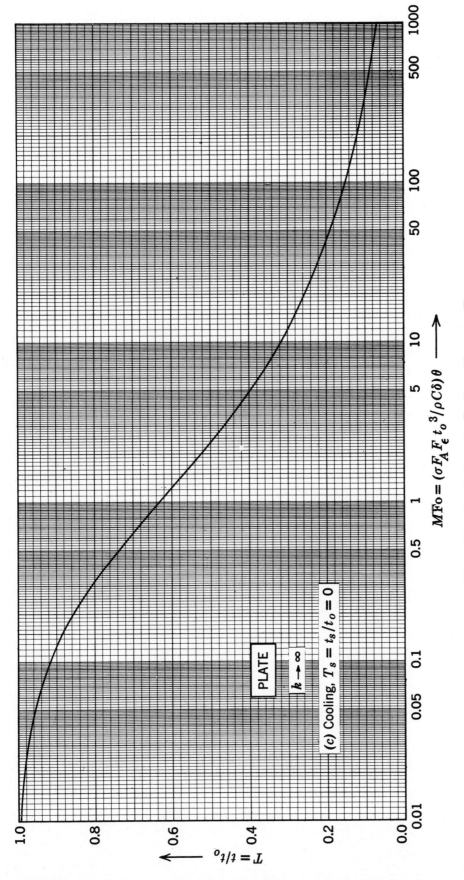

$$M\mathbb{F}o = (\sigma F_A F_\epsilon t_o{}^3 / \rho C\delta)\theta \longrightarrow$$

Chart 53. *Concluded;* (c) Cooling, $T_s = 0$, (E).

8

References

1. Schneider, P. J., *Conduction Heat Transfer*, Addison-Wesley Publishing Company, Reading, Massachusetts, 1955, pp. 232, 243, 248, 265, 277.
2. Thorne, C. J., "Temperature Tables. Part 1. One-Layer Plate, One-Space Variable, Linear," *NAVORD 5562* (*NOTS 1756*), U.S. Naval Ordnance Test Station, China Lake, California, 18 July 1957.
3. Thorne, C. J., and M. D. James, "Temperature Tables. Part 4. Solid Cylinder, One-Space Variable, Linear," *NAVORD 5562* (*NOTS TP 2051*), U. S. Naval Ordnance Test Station, China Lake, California, 18 June 1958.
4. Perry, R. L., and W. P. Berggren, "Transient Heat Conduction in Hollow Cylinders After Sudden Change of Inner-Surface Temperature," University of California Publications in Engineering, Vol. 5, No. 3, *University of California Press*, Berkeley and Los Angeles, 1944.
5. Jaeger, J. C., "Numerical Values for the Temperature in Radial Heat Flow," *Journal of Mathematical Physics*, Vol. 34, No. 4, pp. 316–321, January 1956.
6. Thorne, C. J., and H. C. Morrin, "Temperature Tables. Part 3. One-Layer Cylindrical Shell, External Heating, One-Space Variable, Linear," *NAVORD 5562* (*NOTS TP 2512*), U. S. Naval Ordnance Test Station, China Lake, California, 15 March 1960.
7. Thorne, C. J., and H. C. Morrin, "Temperature Tables. Part 2. One-Layer Cylindrical Shell, Internal Heating, One-Space Variable, Linear," *NAVORD 5562* (*NOTS TP 2511*), U. S. Naval Ordnance Test Station, China Lake, California, 15 March 1960.
8. Williamson, E. D., and L. H. Adams, "Temperature Distribution in Solids During Heating or Cooling," *Physics Review*, Vol. XIV, No. 2, 1919, pp. 99–114.
9. Carslaw, H. S., and J. C. Jaeger, *Conduction of Heat in Solids*, Oxford at the Clarendon Press, Great Britain, 1948, pp. 45, 56, 201, 209, 210, 282.
10. Smithson, R. E., and C. J. Thorne, "Temperature Tables. Part 6. One-Layer Spherical Shell Segments, External Heating, One-Space Variable, Linear," *NAVORD 5562* (*NOTS TP 2088*), U. S. Naval Ordnance Test Station, China Lake, California, 18 September 1958.
11. Smithson, R. E., and Thorne, C. J., "Temperature Tables. Part 5. One-Layer Spherical Shell Segments, Internal Heating, One-Space Variable," *NAVORD 5562* (*NOTS TP 2087*), U. S. Naval Ordnance Test Station, China Lake, California, 18 September 1958.
12. Kirkpatrick, E. T., and W. F. Stokey, "Transient Heat Conduction in Elliptical Plates and Cylinders," *Transactions of the ASME, Journal of Heat Transfer*, Vol. 81, Series C, No. 1, February 1959, pp. 54–60.

13. Jokob, M., *Heat Transfer*, Vol. 1, John Wiley and Sons, New York, 1949, pp. 268, 269.

14. Baxter, A. N., "On the Extension of Transient-Heating Charts for the Semi-Infinite Slab," STL/TN-59-0000-09355, *Space Technology Laboratories, Inc.*, Los Angeles, California, 15 December 1959.

15. Anthony, M. L., "Temperature Distributions in Slabs With a Linear Temperature Rise at One Surface," Part I, Proceedings of the General Discussion on Heat Transfer, *IME, ASME*, 11–13 September 1951, pp. 250–253.

16. Schneider, P. J., and J. J. Brogan, "Temperature Response of a Transpiration-Cooled Plate," *Journal of the American Rocket Society*, Vol. 32, No. 1, January 1962.

17. Holter, W. H., and J. H. Grover, "Insulation Temperature for the Transient Heating of an Insulated Infinite Metal Slab," *Journal of the American Rocket Society*, Vol. 30, No. 9, September 1960, pp. 907–908.

18. Grover, J. H., and W. H. Holter, "Solution of the Transient Heat-Conduction Equation for an Insulated Infinite Metal Slab," *Jet Propulsion*, Vol. 27, No. 12, December 1957, pp. 1249–1252.

19. Mayer, E., "Heat Flow in Composite Slabs," *Journal of the American Rocket Society*, Vol. 22, No. 3, May–June 1952, pp. 150–158.

20. Harris, R. S., Jr., and J. R. Davidson, "An Analysis of Exact and Approximate Equations for the Temperature Distribution in an Insulated Thick Skin Subjected to Aerodynamic Heating," *NASA TN D-519*, Washington, January 1961.

21. Brogan, J. J., and P. J. Schneider, "Heat Conduction in a Series Composite Wall," *Transactions of the ASME, Journal of Heat Transfer*, Vol. 83, Series C, No. 4, November 1961, pp. 506–508.

22. Green, S. W., "Transient Temperature Distribution in An Infinite Flat Plate With Radial Heat Flow," *Royal Aircraft Establishment TN 92*, Farnborough, October 1953.

23. Geckler, R. D., "Transient, Radial Heat Conduction in Hollow Circular Cylinders," *Jet Propulsion*, Vol. 25, No. 1, January 1955, pp. 31–35.

24. Hatch, J. E., and R. L. Schacht, et. al., "Graphical Presentation of Difference Solutions for Transient Radial Heat Conduction in Hollow Cylinders With Heat Transfer at the Inner Radius and Finite Slabs With Heat Transfer at One Boundary," *NASA TR R-56*, Washington, 1960.

25. Roberts, L., "An Approximate Analysis of Unsteady Vaporization Near the Stagnation Point of Blunt Bodies," *NASA TN D-41*, Washington, September 1959.

26. Newman, A. B., "The Temperature-Time Relations Resulting From the Electrical Heating of the Face of a Slab," *Transactions of the AIChE*, Vol. 30, 1934, pp. 598–613.

27. Brooks, W. A., Jr., "Temperature and Thermal-Stress Distributions in Some Structural Elements Heated at a Constant Rate," *NACA TN-4306*, Washington, August 1958.

28. Manos, W. P., and D. E. Taylor, "Transient Heating at an Axisymmetric Stagnation Point with Mass Addition," Part IV, 1961 International Heat Transfer Conference, *ASME, AIChE, IME, ICE*, Boulder, Colorado, August 1961, pp. 731–736.

29. Coulbert, C. D., and W. F. MacInnes, et. al., "Temperature Response of Infinite Flat Plates and Slabs to Heat Inputs of Short Duration at one Surface," *University of California, Department of Engineering*, April 1951.

30. Wilson, L. H., M. Tucker, and W. E. Brandt, Unclassified Appendix of "Atmospheric and Hypersonic Phenomena: Entry Problems — Preliminary Heat Sink Design Studies of the Polaris Re-Entry Body," *1957 BOCA Conference (USN)*, Washington.

31. Kuhn, J. A., "Temperature Distribution in a Finite Slab Caused by a Heat Rate of the Form $q(\theta) = (q_{max}/2)(1 - \cos \omega \theta)$," *Lockheed Aircraft Corporation, Missiles and Space Division*, Sunnyvale, California, TXN/548, 23 January 1961.

32. Thomas, P. D., "Approximate Analytical Solutions to Transient Heat Conduction in Finite Slabs With Arbitrary Heat Input," *Lockheed Aircraft Corporation, Missiles and Space Division*, Sunnyvale, California, TIAD/148, 26 April 1960.

33. Kaye, J., and V. C. M. Yeh, "Design Charts for Transient Temperature Distribution Resulting From Aerodynamic Heating at Supersonic Speeds," *Journal of the Aeronautical Sciences*, Vol. 22, No. 11, November 1955, pp. 755–763.

34. Bergles, A. E., and J. Kaye., "Solutions of the Heat-Conduction Equation With Time-Dependent Boundary Conditions," *Journal of the Aero/Space Sciences*, Vol. 28, No. 3, March 1961, pp. 251–252.

35. Schneider, P. J., "Radiation Cooling of Finite Heat-Conducting Solids," *Journal of the Aero/Space Sciences*," Vol. 27, No. 7, July 1960, pp. 546–548.

36. Clark, S. K., "Heat-up Time of Wire Glow Plugs," *Jet Propulsion*, Vol. 26, No. 4, April 1956, pp. 278–279.

37. Brogan, J. J., "Extensions to a Well-Known Heat Transfer Solution: The Thermal Response of a Thin Skin Exposed to a Constant Temperature Radiation Environment," *Lockheed Aircraft Corporation, Missiles and Space Division*, Sunnyvale, California, AP1/8, 2 June 1961.

38. Robbins, W. H., "Analysis of the Transient Radiation Heat Transfer of an Uncooled Rocket Engine Operating Outside Earth's Atmosphere," *NASA TN D-62*, Washington, December 1959.